B.D.Chaurasia's
HANDBOOK OF
GENERAL
ANATOMY

Whatever a man can conceive and believe.
He can Achieve!

Late Dr. B.D. CHAURASIA
1937-1985

B.D.Chaurasia's
HANDBOOK OF
GENERAL
ANATOMY

Late Dr. B.D. CHAURASIA
M.B., B.S., M.S., Ph.D., F.A.M.S.
Department of Anatomy
G.R. Medical College, Gwalior, India

CBS PUBLISHERS & DISTRIBUTORS
4596, 1-A, 11 Darya Ganj, New Delhi - 110 002, (INDIA)

DEDICATED TO MY TEACHER
SHRI UMA SHANKAR NAGAYACH

ISBN : 81-239-0421-5

First Edition : 1978
Reprint : 1980, 1981
Second Edition : 1983
Reprint : 1985, 1987, 1989, 1991, 1992, 1994
Third Edition : 1996
Reprint : 1998, 1999, 2000, 2001, 2002, 2003, 2004, 2005 2006
Reprint : 2007

© Publishers and Author

Third Edition revised by Dr. Krishna Garg, Professor of Anatomy,
Lady Hardinge Medical College, New Delhi 110 001, India

Published by Satish Kumar Jain for CBS Publishers & Distributors,
4596, 1-A, 11 Darya Ganj, New Delhi - 110 002, India.

Laser typeset at :
Rafah Typesetters, Delhi - 110 092

Printed at :
India Binding House, Noida (U.P.)

Preface to the Third Edition

I feel a sense of pride and enthusiasm in presenting to you the revised third edition of this popular book. Now, simple diagrams extensively illustrate each chapter. Once initial interest to read text supplemented by diagrams is developed, learning general anatomy is hardly problematic.

"Anatomical word meanings and Historical names" is a unique feature of this revised edition and this new chapter provides the English language meaning to anatomical jargon. The help of Ms. S. Priya, professional student during 1990-91 is being acknowledged in concising this dictionary.

The readers are welcome to send their suggestions and comments, which I believe will definitely lead to improvement of the book.

Krishna Garg

Preface to the Second Edition

This edition incorporates a number of new features which were mostly suggested by the readers of the first edition. The simple line diagrams have been introduced at appropriate places to facilitate understanding of the subject. An entirely new chapter on the 'principles of radiography' has been added. The greater part of the text has been revised and rewritten in view of the recent advances in various fields of the subject. Though this has resulted in a little elaboration of the text, still it is concise enough for the students to read through and grasp the matter. The original pattern of the book has been carefully retained because it has proved very helpful in quick retention of facts in the memory and their prompt .recollection when desired. The authority at a number of places has been duly cited, and at the end of each chapter the 'references and suggestions for additional reading' have been given.

I express my sincere thanks to all the readers who have encouraged me by approving the usefulness of the book, and by writing me their suggestions to improve it.

Gwalior
January, 1983

B.D. CHAURASIA

Preface to the First Edition

This handbook of general anatomy has been written to meet the requirements of students who are newly admitted to a medical college. It thoroughly introduces the greater part of medical terminology, as well as the various structures which constitute the human body. On account of the late admissions and the shorter time now available for teaching anatomy, the coverage of general anatomy seems to suffer maximum. Since it lays down the foundation of the whole subject of medicine, it was felt necessary to produce a short, simple and comprehensive handbook on this neglected, though important, aspect of the subject. It has been written in a simple language, with the text classified in small parts to make it easier for the students to follow and remember. It is hoped that this will prove quite useful to the medical students.

Gwalior
November, 1978

B.D. CHAURASIA

Contents

1

Introduction

Human anatomy is the science which deals with the structure of the human body. The term, 'anatomy', is derived from a Greek word, "anatome", meaning cutting up. The term 'dissection' is a Latin equivalent of the Greek anatome. However, the two words, anatomy and dissection, are not synonymous. Dissection is a mere technique, whereas anatomy is a wide field of study.

Anatomy forms firm foundation of the whole art of medicine, and introduces the student to the greater part of medical terminology. "Anatomy is to physiology as geography is to history, i.e., it describes the theatre in which the action takes place."

SUBDIVISIONS OF ANATOMY

Initially, anatomy was studied mainly by dissection. But the scope of modern anatomy has become very wide because it is now studied by all possible techniques which can enlarge the boundaries of the anatomical knowledge.

Fig. 1.1. Subdivisions of Anatomy.

Fig. 1.1 shows some of the subdivisions of Anatomy, e.g., thorax in A, lower limb in N, brain in A, arteries in T, histology in O, upper limb and living anatomy in M, genetics and embryology in Y.

The main subdivisions of anatomy are listed below :

1. **Cadaveric anatomy** is studied on dead bodies usually with the naked eye (*macroscopic* or *gross anatomy*). This can be done by one of

the two approaches (a) In '*regional anatomy*' the body is studied in parts, like the upper limb, lower limb, thorax, abdomen, head and neck, and brain; (b) in '*systemic anatomy*' the body is studied in systems, like the skeletal system (osteology), muscular system (myology), articulatory system (arthrology or syndesmology), vascular system (angiology), nervous system (neurology), and respiratory, digestive, urogenital and endocrine systems (splanchnology). The locomotor system includes osteology, arthrology and myology (Figs. 1.2 & 1.3).

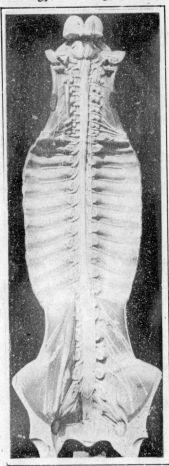

Fig. 1.2. Spinal cord and spinal nerves (nervous system).

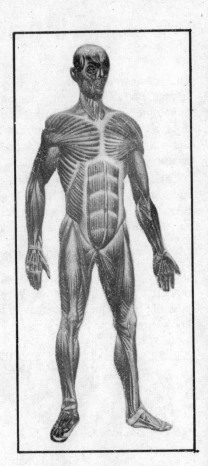

Fig. 1.3. Muscular system.

2. **Living anatomy** is studied on living human beings, by inspection, palpation, percussion, auscultation, endoscopy (bronchoscopy, gastroscopy, sigmoidoscopy, cystoscopy, etc.) radiography, electromyography, etc. (Fig. 1.4).

3. **Embryology (developmental anatomy)** is the study of the pre-natal and postnatal developmental changes in an individual. The developmental history is called 'ontogeny'. The evolutionary history, on the other hand, is called 'phylogeny'.

4. **Histology (microscopic anatomy)** is the study of structures with the aid of a microscope.

5. **Surface anatomy (topographic anatomy)** is the study of deeper parts of the body in relation to the skin surface. It is helpful in clinical practice and surgical operations (Fig. 1.5).

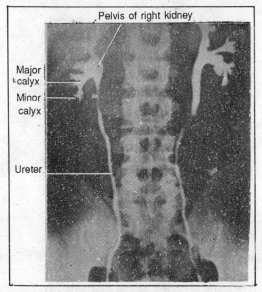

Pelvis of right kidney

Major calyx

Minor calyx

Ureter

Fig. 1.4. A pyelogram.

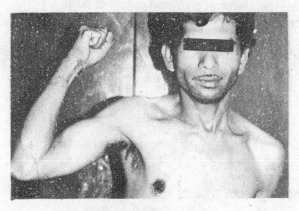

Fig. 1.5. Surface anatomy.

6. **Radiographic anatomy** is the study of deeper organs by plain and contrast radiography (Fig. 1.6).

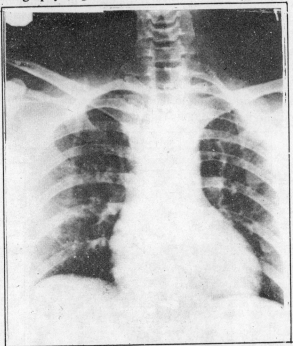

Fig. 1.6. Radiological anatomy.

7. **Comparative anatomy** is the study of anatomy of the other animals to explain the changes in form, structure and function (morphology) of different parts of the human body.

8. **Physical anthropology** deals with the external features and measurements of different races and groups of people, and with the study of the prehistoric remains (Fig. 1.7).

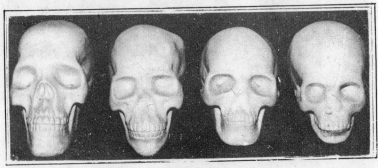

Fig. 1.7. Physical anthropology.

9. **Applied anatomy (clinical anatomy)** deals with application of the anatomical knowledge to the medical and surgical practice.

10. **Experimental anatomy** is the study of the factors which influence and determine the form, structure and function of different parts of the body.

HISTORY OF ANATOMY

1. Greek Period (B.C.)

Hippocrates of Cos (circa 400 B.C.), the 'Father of Medicine', is regarded as one of the founders of anatomy. Parts of Hippocratic collection are the earliest anatomical descriptions.

Herophilus of Chalcedon (circa 300 B.C.) is called the "father of anatomy". He was a Greek physician, and was one of the first to dissect the human body. He distinguished cerebrum from cerebellum, nerves from tendons, arteries from veins, and the motor from sensory nerves. He described and named the parts of eye, meninges, torcular Herophili, fourth ventricle with calamus scriptorius, hyoid bone, duodenum, prostate gland, etc. We owe to him the first description of the lacteals. Herophilus was a very successful teacher, and wrote a book on anatomy, '*A special treatise of the eyes*', and a popular handbook for midwives.

2. Roman Period (A.D.)

Galen of Pergamum, Asia Minor (circa 130-200 A.D.), the "prince of physicians", practised medicine at Rome. He was the foremost practitioner of his days and the first experimental Physiologist. He wrote voluminously, and theorized and dogmatized on many medical subjects, like anatomy, physiology, pathology, symptomatology, and treatment. He demonstrated and wrote on anatomy, '*De anatomicis administrationibus*'. His teachings were followed and considered as the infallible authority on the subject for nearly 15 centuries.

3. Fourteenth Century

Mundinus or **Mondino d'Luzzi** (1276-1326), the 'restorer of anatomy', was an Italian anatomist and professor of anatomy at Bologna. He wrote a book '*Anathomia*' which was the standard anatomical text for over a century. He taught anatomy by dissection for which his text was used as a guide. He was the most renowned anatomist before Vesalius.

4. Fifteenth Century

Leonardo da Vinci of Italy (1452-1519), the originator of cross-sectional anatomy, was one of the greatest geniuses the world has known. He was a master of art, and contributed substantially in mathematics, science and engineering. He was the first to describe the moderator band of the right ventricle. The most admirable of his works are the drawings of the things he observed with perfection and fidelity. His 60 notebooks containing 500 diagrams were published in 1898.

5. Sixteenth Century

Vesalius (1514-1564), the 'reformer of anatomy', was German in origin, Belgian (Brussels) by birth, and found an Italian (Padua) university favourable for his work. He was professor of anatomy at Padua. He is regarded as the founder of modern anatomy because he taught that anatomy could be learned only through dissections. He opposed and corrected the erroneous concepts of Galen and fought against his authority, thus reviving anatomy after a deadlock of about 15 centuries. His great anatomical treatise *"De Febricia Humani Corporis"*, written in seven volumes, revolutionized the teaching of anatomy and remained as authoritative text for two centuries.

Vesalius studied first at Louvain and then at Paris under Gunther and Sylvius. Eustachius was the rival of Vesalius. The followers of Vesalius included Servetus, Columbus, Fallopius, Varolio, Vidius, etc.; all of them lived during 16th century.

6. Seventeenth Century

William Harvey (1578-1657) was an English physician who discovered the circulation of blood, and published it as *"Anatomical Exercise on the Motion of the Heart and Blood in Animals"*. He also published a book on embryology.

The other events of this century included : (a) the first recorded human dissection in 1638 in Massachusetts; (b) foundation of microscopic anatomy by Malpighi; and (c) introduction of alcohol as a preservative.

7. Eighteenth Century

William Hunter (1718-1783) was a London anatomist and obstetrician. He introduced the present day embalming with the help of Harvey's discovery, and founded with his younger brother (John Hunter) the famous Hunterian museum.

8. Nineteenth Century

Dissection by medical students was made compulsory in Edinburgh (1826) and Maryland (1833). Burke and Hare scandal of 16 murders took place in Edinburgh in 1828. Warburton Anatomy Act (1932) was passed in England under which the unclaimed bodies were made available for dissection. The 'act' was passed in America (Massachusetts) in 1831. Formalin was used as a fixative in 1890s, x-rays were discovered by Roentgen in 1895. Various endoscopes were devised between 1819 and 1899. The anatomical societies were founded in Germany (1886), Britain (1887) and America (1888).

The noted anatomists of this century include Astley Cooper (1768-1841; British surgeon), Cuvier (1769-1832; French naturalist), Meckel (1724-1774; German anatomist), and Henry Gray (1827-1861; the author of Gray's Anatomy).

ANATOMICAL NOMENCLATURE

Galen (2nd century) wrote his book in Greek, and Vesalius (16th century) did it in Latin. Most of the anatomical terms, therefore, are either in Greek or Latin. By 19th century about 30,000 anatomical terms were in use in the books and journals. In 1895, the German Anatomical Society held a meeting in Basle, and approved a list of about 5000 terms known as **Basle Nomina Anatomica** (*BNA*). The following six rules were laid down to be followed strictly : (1) each part shall have only one name; (2) each term shall be in Latin; (3) each term shall be as short and simple as possible; (4) the terms shall be merely memory signs; (5) the related terms shall be similar, e.g., femoral artery, femoral vein, and femoral nerve; and (6) the adjectives shall be arranged as opposites, e.g., major and minor, superior and inferior.

BNA was revised in 1933 by a committee of the Anatomical Society of Great Britain and Ireland in a meeting held at Birmingham. The revised BNA was named as **Birmingham Revision** (*BR*). An independent revision of the BNA was also done by German anatomists in 1935, and was known as **Jena Nomina Anatomica** (*JNA* or *INA*). However, the BR and INA found only local and restricted acceptance.

In 1950, it was agreed at an International Congress of Anatomists held at Oxford that a further attempt should be made to establish a generally acceptable international nomenclature. In the Sixth International Congress of Anatomists held at Paris (1955), a somewhat conservative revision of BNA with many terms from BR and INA was approved. Minor revisions and corrections were made at the International Congresses held in New York (1960), and Wiesbaden, Germany (1965), and the 3rd edition of **Nomina Anatomica** (Ed. G.A.G. Mitchell, 1968) was published by the Excerpta Medica Foundation.

The drafts on *Nomina Histologica* and *Nomina Embryologica* prepared by the subcommittee of the International Anatomical Nomenclature Committee (IANC) were approved in a plenary session of the Eleventh International Congress of Anatomists held in Leningrad in 1970. After a critical revision, the 4th edition of Nomina Anatomica (Ed. Roger Warwick, 1977) containing Nomina Histologica and Nomina Embryologica was published by the same publisher. The 5th edition of Nomina Anatomica is due to appear shortly.

DESCRIPTIVE TERMS

1. Terms Used for Describing the Position of the Body

(a) **Anatomical position.** In this position, the body is erect, the eyes look straight to the front, the upper limbs hang by the side of the trunk with the palms directed forwards, and the lower limbs are parallel with the toes pointing forwards (Fig. 1.8).

All structures are described presuming the body in anatomical position, although during study the body may be placed in any position.

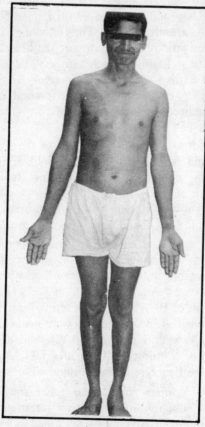

Fig. 1.8. Anatomical position.

(b) **Supine position.** Lying down (recumbent) position with the face directed upwards (Fig. 1.9).

(c) **Prone position.** Lying down (recumbent) position with the face directed downwards (Fig. 1.10).

(d) **Lithotomy position.** Lying supine with the buttocks at the edge of the table, the hips and knees fully flexed, and the feet strapped in position.

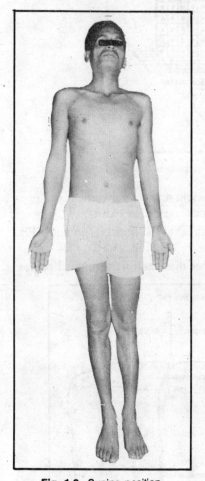

Fig. 1.9. Supine position.

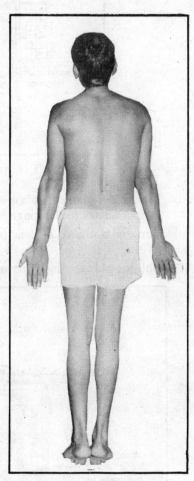

Fig. 1.10. Prone position.

2. Anatomical Planes

(a) **Median or midsagittal plane** divides the body into right and left halves (Fig. 1.11).

(b) **Sagittal plane.** Any plane parallel to the median plane (Fig. 1.11).

(c) **Coronal or frontal plane.** A vertical plane at right angles to the median plane (Fig. 1.11).

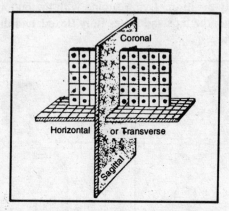

Fig. 1.11. Three planes.

(d) **Transverse plane.** A plane at right angles to a vertical plane, or at right angles to the longitudinal axis of any part.

(e) **Horizontal plane.** A plane parallel to the horizon (ground) (Fig. 1.12).

(f) **Oblique plane.** Any plane other than the forementioned planes.

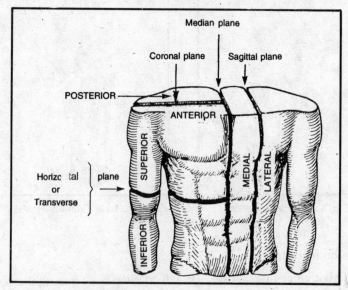

Fig. 1.12. The three planes in the body.

3. Terms of Relation Commonly Used in Gross Anatomy (Fig. 1.13)

(a) **Anterior** — Towards the front.
(b) **Posterior** — Towards the back.
(c) **Superior** — Towards the head.
(d) **Inferior** — Towards the feet.
(e) **Medial** — Towards the median plane.
(f) **Lateral** — Away from the median plane.

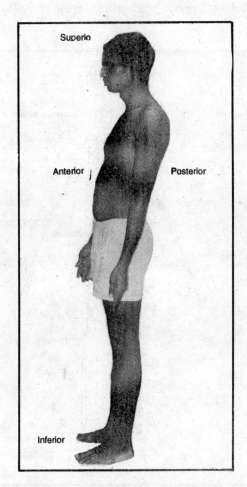

Fig. 1.13. The terms for gross anatomy.

4. Terms of Relation Commonly Used in Embryology and Comparative Anatomy, but sometimes in Gross Anatomy

(a) **Ventral** — Towards the belly (like anterior).

(b) **Dorsal** — Towards the back (like posterior).

(c) **Cranial or Rostral** — Towards the head (like superior).

(d) **Caudal** — Towards the tail.

5. Special Terms for Limbs (Fig. 1.14)

(a) **Proximal** — Nearer to the trunk.

(b) **Distal** — Away from the trunk.

(c) **Radial** — The outer border in the upper limb.

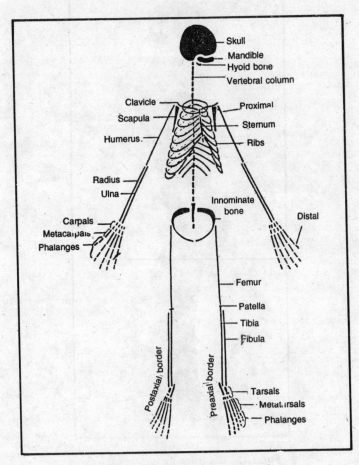

Fig. 1.14. The terms for limbs.

(d) **Ulnar** — The inner border in the upper limb.

(e) **Tibial** — The inner border in the lower limb.

(f) **Fibular** — The outer border in the lower limb.

(g) **Preaxial border** — The outer border in the upper limb, and the inner border in the lower limb.

(h) **Postaxial border** — The inner border in the upper limb, and the outer border in the lower limb.

(i) **Flexor surface** — The anterior surface in the upper limb, and the posterior surface in the lower limb.

(j) **Extensor surface** — The posterior surface in the upper limb, and the anterior surface in the lower limb.

(k) **Palmar or Volar** — Pertaining to (towards) the palm of the hand.

(l) **Plantar** — Pertaining to (towards) the sole of the foot.

6. Certain Other Terms

A. Terms used for hollow organs :

(a) **Interior** or inner;

(b) **Exterior** or outer;

(c) **Invagination** or inward protrusion; and

(d) **Evagination** or outward protrusion.

B. Terms used for solid organs :

(a) **Superficial**, towards the surface; and

(b) **Deep**, inner to the surface.

C. Terms used to indicate the side :

(a) **Ipsilateral** — of the same side; and

(b) **Contralateral** — of the opposite side.

7. Terms Used for Describing Muscles

(a) **Origin.** The end of a muscle which is relatively fixed during its contraction.

(b) **Insertion.** The end of a muscle which moves during its contraction.

The two terms, origin and insertion, are sometimes interchangeable, when the origin moves and the insertion is fixed.

(c) **Belly.** The fleshy and contractile part of a muscle.

(d) **Tendon.** The fibrous, noncontractile and cord-like part of a muscle.

(e) **Aponeurosis.** The flattened tendon.

(f) **Raphe.** A fibrous band made up of interdigitating fibres of the tendons or aponeuroses. Unlike a ligament, it is stretchable. Ligaments are fibrous, inelastic bands which connect two segments of a joint.

8. Terms Used for Describing Movements (Figs. 1.15-1.24)

(a) **Flexion.** Approximation of the flexor surfaces whereby the angle of the joint is reduced.

(b) **Extension.** Approximation of the extensor surfaces whereby the angle of the joint is increased. It is opposite to flexion.

(c) **Adduction.** Movement towards the central axis.

(d) **Abduction.** Movement away from the central axis. It is opposite to adduction.

(e) **Medial rotation.** Inward rotation.

(f) **Lateral rotation.** Outward rotation.

(g) **Circumduction.** Various combinations of the foregoing movements (a to d).

(h) **Pronation.** Rotation of the forearm so that the palm is turned backwards.

(i) **Supination.** Rotation of the forearm so that the palm is turned forwards.

(j) **Protraction.** Forwards protrusion.

(k) **Retraction.** Movement reverse of protraction.

9. Terms Used for Describing Vessels

(a) **Arteries** carry oxygenated blood away from the heart, with the exception of the pulmonary and umbilical arteries which carry deoxygenated blood. Arteries resemble trees because they have branches (arterioles).

(b) **Veins** carry deoxygenated blood towards the heart, with the exception of the pulmonary and umbilical veins which carry oxygenated blood. Veins resemble rivers because they have tributaries (venules).

(c) **Capillaries** are networks of microscopic vessels connecting arterioles to venules.

(d) **Anastomosis** is a precapillary or postcapillary communication between the neighbouring vessels.

11. Terms Used for Describing Bony Features (Figs. 1.25 & 1.26)

(A) **Elevations :** (a) *Linear elevation* may be a line, lip, ridge, or crest. (b) *Sharp elevation* may be a spine, styloid process, cornu

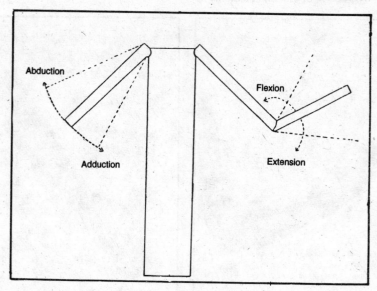

Fig. 1.15. Angular movement.

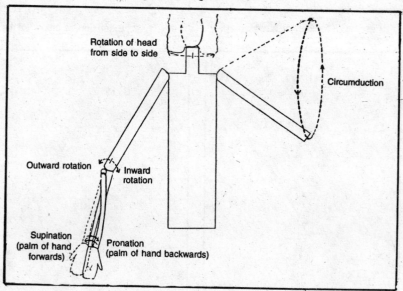

Fig. 1.16. Rotary movements.

(horn), or <u>hamulus</u>. (c) *Rounded* or *irregular elevation* may be a <u>tubercle</u>, tuberosity, <u>epicondyle</u>, <u>malleolus</u>, or <u>trochanter</u>. A ramus is a broad arm or process projecting from the main part or body of the bone.

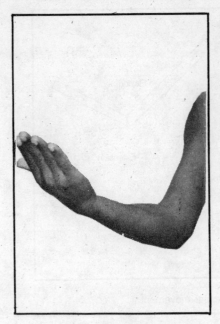

Fig. 1.17. Flexion at elbow joint.

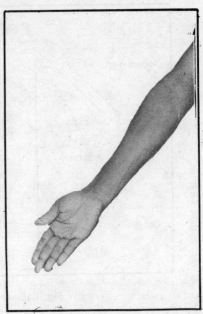

Fig. 1.18. Extension at elbow joint.

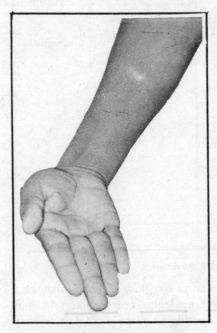

Fig. 1.19. Adduction at wrist joint.

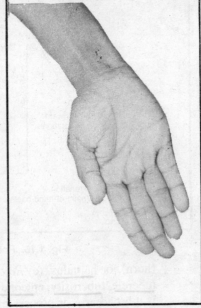

Fig. 1.20. Abduction at wrist joint.

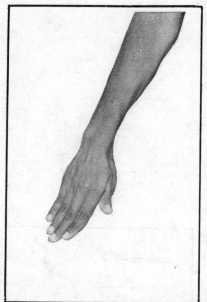

Fig. 1.21. Pronation of forearm.

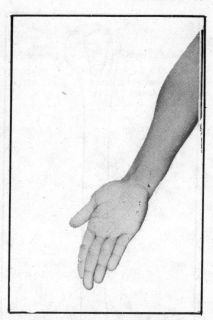

Fig. 1.22. Supination of forearm.

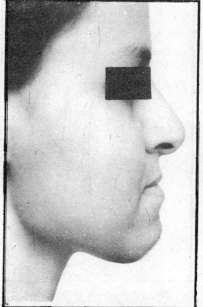

Fig. 1.23. Protraction of jaw.

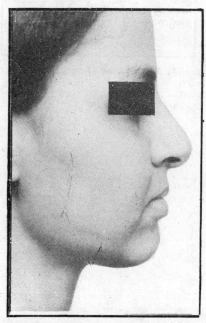

Fig. 1.24. Retraction of jaw.

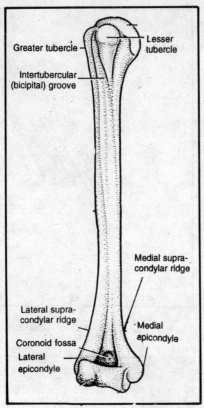

Greater tubercle

Lesser tubercle

Intertubercular (bicipital) groove

Medial supra-condylar ridge

Lateral supra-condylar ridge

Medial epicondyle

Coronoid fossa

Lateral epicondyle

(A) Anterior view of right humerus;

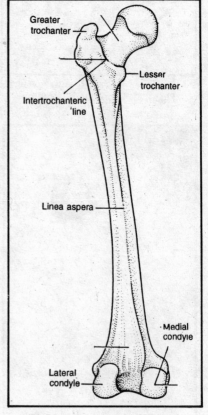

Greater trochanter

Lesser trochanter

Intertrochanteric line

Linea aspera

Medial condyle

Lateral condyle

(B) Posterior view of left femur.

Fig. 1.25. (A) Anterior view of right humerus; (B) Posterior view of left femur.

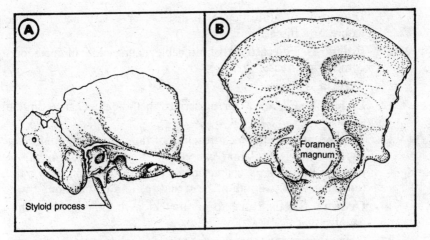

Fig. 1.26. (A) Styloid process; (B) Foramen magnum.

(B) **Depressions** may be a pit, impression, fovea, fossa, groove (sulcus), or notch (incisura).

(C) **Openings** may be a foramen, canal, hiatus, or aqueduct.

(D) **Cavities :** A large cavity within a bone is called sinus, cell or antrum.

(E) **Smooth articular areas** may be a facet, condyle, head, capitulum, or trochlea.

12. Terms Used in Applied (Clinical) Anatomy

1. The suffix, '**-itis**', means inflammation, e.g., appendicitis, tonsillitis, arthritis, neuritis, dermatitis, etc.

2. The suffix, '**-ectomy**', means removal from the body, e.g., appendicectomy, tonsillectomy, gastrectomy, nephrectomy, etc.

3. The suffix, '**-otomy**', means to open and then close a hollow organ, e.g., laparotomy, hysterotomy, cystotomy, cystolithotomy, etc.

4. The suffix, '**-ostomy**', means to open hollow organ and leave it open, e.g., cystostomy, colostomy, tracheostomy, etc.

5. The suffix, '**-oma**', means a tumour, e.g., lipoma, osteoma, neurofibroma, haemangioma, carcinoma, etc.

6. **Puberty.** The age at which the secondary sexual characters develop, being 12-15 years in girls and 13-16 years in boys.

7. **Symptoms** are subjective complaints of the patient about his disease.

8. **Signs (physical signs)** are objective findings of the doctor on the patient.

9. **Diagnosis.** Identification of a disease, or determination of the nature of a disease.

10. **Prognosis.** Forecasting the probable course and ultimate outcome of a disease.

11. **Pyrexia.** Fever.

12. **Lesion.** Injury, or a circumscribed pathologic change in the tissues.

13. **Inflammation** is the local reaction of the tissues to an injury or an abnormal stimulation caused by a physical, chemical, or biologic agent. It is characterized by : (a) swelling; (b) pain; (c) redness; (d) warmth of heat; and (e) loss of function.

14. **Oedema.** Swelling due to accumulation of fluid in the extracellular space.

15. **Thrombosis.** Intravascular coagulation (solidification) of blood.

16. **Embolism.** Occlusion of a vessel by a detached and circulating thrombus (embolus).

17. **Haemorrhage.** Bleeding which may be external or internal.

18. **Ulcer.** A localized breach (gap, erosion) in the surface continuity of the skin or mucous membrane.

19. **Sinus.** A blind track (open at one end) lined by epithelium.

20. **Fistula.** A track open at both the ends and lined by epithelium.

21. **Necrosis.** Local death of a tissue or organ due to irreversible damage to the nucleus.

22. **Degeneration.** A retrogressive change causing deterioration in the structural and functional qualities. It is a reversible process, but may end in necrosis.

23. **Gangrene.** A form of necrosis (death) combined with putrefaction.

24. **Infarction.** Death (necrosis) of a tissue due to sudden obstruction of its artery of supply (often an end-artery).

25. **Atrophy.** Diminution in the size of cells, tissue, organ, or a part due to loss of its nutrition.

26. **Dystrophy.** Diminution in the size due to defective nutrition.

27. **Hypertrophy.** Increase in the size without any increase in the number of cells.

28. **Hyperplasia.** Increase in the size due to increase in the number of cells.

29. **Hypoplasia.** Incomplete development.

30. **Aplasia.** Failure of development.

31. **Syndrome.** A group of diverse symptoms and signs constituting together the picture of a disease.

32. **Paralysis.** Loss of motor power (movement) of a part of body due to denervation or primary disease of the muscles.
33. **Hemiplegia.** Paralysis of one-half of the body.
34. **Paraplegia.** Paralysis of both the lower limbs.
35. **Monoplegia.** Paralysis of any one limb.
36. **Quadriplegia.** Paralysis of all the four limbs.
37. **Anaesthesia.** Loss of the touch sensibility.
38. **Analgesia.** Loss of the pain sensibility.
39. **Thermanaesthesia.** Loss of the temperature sensibility.
40. **Hyperaesthesia.** Abnormally increased sensibility.
41. **Paraesthesia.** Perverted feeling of sensations.
42. **Coma.** Deep unconsciousness.
43. **Tumour (neoplasm).** A circumscribed, noninflammatory, abnormal growth arising from the body tissues.
44. **Benign.** Mild (illness or growth) which does not endanger life.
45. **Malignant.** Severe form of illness or growth, which is resistant to treatment and ends in death.
46. **Carcinoma.** Malignant growth arising from the epithelium (ectoderm or endoderm).
47. **Sarcoma.** Malignant growth arising from connective tissue (mesoderm).
48. **Cancer.** A general term used to indicate any malignant neoplasm which shows invasiveness and results in death of the patient.
49. **Metastasis.** Spread of a local disease (like the cancer cells) to distant parts of the body.
50. **Convalescence.** The recovery period between the end of a disease and restoration to complete health.
51. **Therapy.** Medical treatment.

ARRANGEMENT OF STRUCTURES IN THE BODY FROM WITHIN OUTWARDS

1. Bones form the supporting framework of the body.
2. Muscles are attached to bones.
3. Blood vessels, nerves and lymphatics form neurovascular bundles which course in between the muscles, along the fascial planes.
4. The thoracic and abdominal cavities contain several internal organs called viscera.
5. The whole body has three general coverings, namely (a) skin; (b) superficial fascia; and (c) deep fascia.

REFERENCES AND SUGGESTIONS
FOR ADDITIONAL READING

Field, E.J. and Harrison, R.J. (1957). *Anatomical Terms; Their Origin and Derivation*, 2nd ed. Heffer, Cambridge.

Major, R.H. (1954). *A History of Medicine*, 2 volumes. Thomas, Springfield.

Singer, C, (1957). *A Short History of Anatomy From the Greeks to Harvey*. Dover, New York.

Singh, S. (1972). Grave-robbers all. *Science Reporter*, 9 : 492-493.

Singh, S. (1972). The Illustrious Hunters and the Anatomy Museums. *Indian Med. Gaz.*, 12 : 62-66.

Singh, S. (1973). Cadaveric supply for anatomical dissections, a historical review. *Indian J. History Med.* 18 : 35-39.

Singh, S. (1974). Susruta, pioneer in human dissections. *Souvenir, Anat. Soc. India*, 31-32.

2

Skeleton

Skeleton includes bones and cartilages. It forms the main supporting framework of the body, and is primarily designed for a more effective production of movements by the attached muscles.

BONES

Synonyms

1. Os (L); 2. Osteon (G). Compare with the terms, osteology, ossification, osteomyelitis, osteomalacia, osteoma, osteotomy, etc.

Definition

Bone is a connective tissue (1/3), impregnated with calcium salts (2/3). The inorganic calcium salts (mainly calcium phosphate, partly calcium carbonate, and traces of other salts) make it hard and rigid, which can afford resistance to compressive forces of weight-bearing and impact forces of jumping. The organic connective tissue (collagen fibres) makes it tough and resilient (flexible), which can afford resistance to tensile forces. In strength, bone is comparable to iron and steel.

Despite its hardness and high calcium content the bone is very much living tissue. It is highly vascular, with a constant turn-over of its calcium content. It shows a characteristic pattern of growth. It is subject to disease and heals after a fracture. It has greater regenerative power than any other tissue of the body, except blood. It can mould itself according to changes in stress and strain it bears. It shows disuse atrophy and overuse hypertrophy.

Divisions of the Skeletal System (Fig. 2.1)

Regions of the Skeleton	Number of Bones
AXIAL SKELETON	
Skull	
Cranium	8
Face	14
Hyoid	1
Auditory ossicles (3 in each ear)	6
Vertebral column	26
Thorax	
Sternum	1
Ribs	24
	80
APPENDICULAR SKELETON	
Pectoral (shoulder) girdles	
Clavicle	2
Scapula	2
Upper extremities	
Humerus	2
Ulna	2
Radius	2
Carpals	16
Metacarpals	10
Phalanges	28
Pelvic (hip) girdle	
Coxal, pelvic, or hip bone	2
Lower extremities	
Femur	2
Fibula	2
Tibia	2
Patella	2
Tarsals	14
Metatarsals	10
Phalanges	28
	126 Total = 206

Functions

1. Bones give shape and support to the body, and resist all forms of stress.

2. They provide surface for the <u>attachment of muscles</u>, <u>tendons</u>, <u>ligaments</u>, etc.

3. They serve as levers for <u>muscular actions</u>.

4. The skull, vertebral column and thoracic cage <u>protect</u> brain, spinal cord and thoracic viscera, respectively.

5. Bone marrow <u>manufactures</u> blood cells.

6. Bones <u>store 97%</u> of the body <u>calcium</u> and <u>phosphorus</u>.

7. Bone marrow contains reticulo-endothelial cells which are phago-cytic in nature and take part in <u>immune responses</u> of the body.

8. The larger paranasal air sinuses <u>affect</u> the timber of the voice.

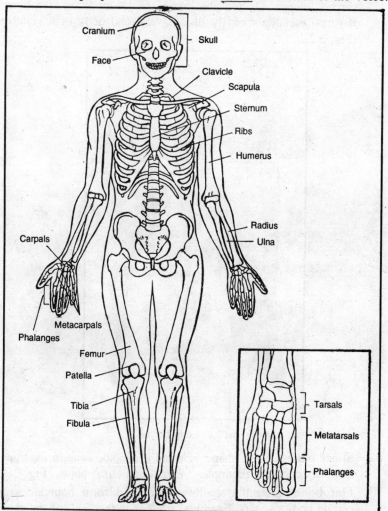

Fig. 2.1. Human skeleton.

CLASSIFICATION OF BONES

A. According to Shape

1. **Long bones.** Each long bone has an elongated shaft (diaphysis) and two expanded ends (epiphyses) which are smooth and articular. The shaft typically has 3 surfaces separated by 3 borders, a central medullary cavity, and a nutrient foramen directed away from the growing end. Examples : (a) typical long bones, like humerus, radius, ulna, femur, tibia and fibula; (b) miniature long bones have only one epiphysis, like metacarpals, metatarsals and phalanges; and (c) modified long bones have no medullary cavity like clavicle and body of a vertebra (Fig. 2.2).

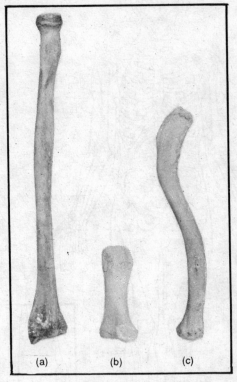

(a)   (b)   (c)

Fig. 2.2. Long bones.

2. **Short bones.** Their shape is usually cuboid, cuneiform, trapezoid, or scaphoid. Examples : carpal and tarsal bones (Fig. 2.3).

3. **Flat bones** resemble shallow plates and form boundaries of certain body cavities. Examples : bones in the vault of the skull, ribs, sternum and scapula (Fig. 2.4).

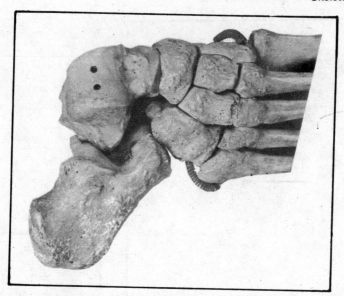

Fig. 2.3. Small bones.

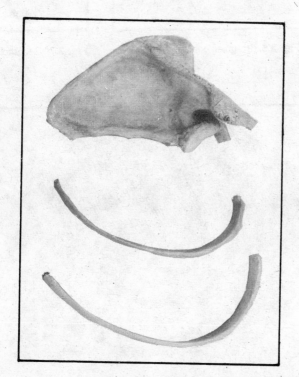

Fig. 2.4. Flat bones.

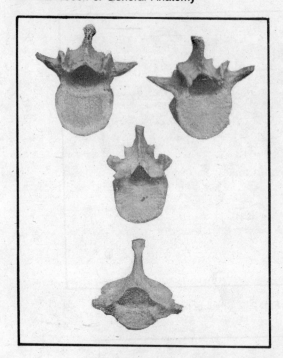

Fig. 2.5. Irregular bones.

Fig. 2.7. Sesamoid bone.

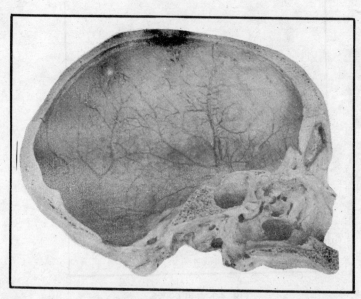

Fig. 2.6. Pneumatic bones.

4. **Irregular bones.** Examples : vertebra, hip bone, and bones in the base of the skull (Fig. 2.5).

5. **Pneumatic bones.** Certain irregular bones contain large air spaces lined by epithelium. Examples : maxilla, sphenoid, ethmoid, etc. They make the skull light in weight, help in resonance of voice, and act as air conditioning chambers for the inspired air (Fig. 2.6).

6. **Sesamoid bones.** These are bony nodules found embedded in the tendons or joint capsules. They have no periosteum and ossify after birth. They are related to an articular or nonarticular bony surface, and the surfaces of contact are covered with hyaline cartilage and lubricated by a bursa or synovial membrane. Examples : patella, pisiform, fabella, etc. (Fig. 2.7).

   Functions of the sesamoid bones are not definitely known. Their possible functions are :

   (a) to resist pressure;

   (b) to minimise friction;

   (c) to alter the direction of pull of the muscle; and

   (d) to maintain the local circulation.

7. **Accessory (supernumerary) bones** are not always present. They may occur as ununited epiphyses developed from extra centres of ossification. Examples : sutural bones, os trigonum, os vesalianum, etc. In medicolegal practice, accessory bones may be mistaken for fractures. However, these are often bilateral, and have smooth surfaces without any callus.

B. Developmental Classification

1. **Membrane (dermal) bones** ossify in membrane (intramembranous or mesenchymal ossification), and are thus derived from mesenchymal condensations. Examples : bones of the vault of skull and facial bones.

   A defect in membranous ossification causes a rare syndrome called cleidocranial dysostosis. It is characterized by three cardinal features : (a) varying degrees of aplasia of the clavicles; (b) increase in the transverse diameter of cranium, and (c) retardation in fontanelle ossification (Srivastava et al., 1971). It may be hereditary or environmental in origin.

2. **Cartilaginous bones** ossify in cartilage (intracartilaginous or endochondral ossification), and are thus derived from preformed cartilaginous models. Examples : bones of limbs, vertebral column and thoracic cage.

A defect in endochondral ossification causes a common type of dwarfism called achondroplasia, in which the limbs are short, but the trunk is normal. It is transmitted as a Mendelian dominant character.

3. **Membrano-cartilaginous bones** ossify partly in membrane **and** partly in cartilage. Examples : clavicle, mandible, occipital, temporal, sphenoid, etc.

C. Regional Classification

1. **Axial skeleton** includes skull, vertebral column, and thoracic cage.
2. **Appendicular skeleton** includes bones of the limbs.

D. Structural Classification

I. *Macroscopically*, the architecture of bone may be compact or cancellous.

1. **Compact bone** is dense in texture like ivory, but is extremely porous. It is best developed in the cortex of the long bones. This is an adaptation to bending and twisting forces (a combination of compression, tension and shear).

2. **Cancellous spongy**, or **trabecular bone** is open in texture, and is made up of a meshwork of trabeculae (rods and plates) between which are marrow containing spaces. The trabecular meshworks are of three primary types, namely, (a) meshwork of rods, (b) meshwork of rods and plates, and (c) meshwork of plates (Singh, 1978). Cancellous bone is an adaptation to compressive forces.

Bones are marvellously constructed to combine strength, elasticity and lightness in weight. Though the architecture of bone may be modified by mechanical forces, the form of the bone is primarily determined by heredity.

According to *Wolff's law* (Trajectory Theory of Wolff, 1892), the bone formation is directly proportional to stress and strain. The tensile force favours bone formation, whereas compressive force favours bone resorption. This theory has been severely criticized and is no longer accepted without reservation. In fact, both the tensile and compressive forces can stimulate bone formation in proper conditions.

The architecture of cancellous bone is often interpreted in terms of the trajectorial theory. Thus the arrangement of bony trabeculae (lamellae) is governed by the lines of maximal internal stress in the bone. *Pressure lamellae* are arranged parallel to the line of weight transmission, whereas *tension lamellae* are arranged at right angles to pressure lamellae. The compact arrangement of pressure lamellae forms bony buttresses for additional support, like calcar femorale (Fig. 2.8).

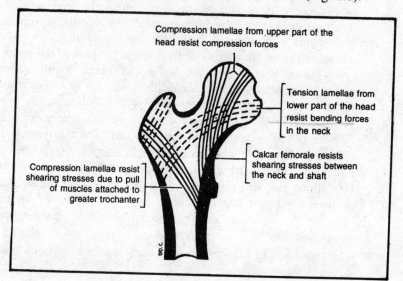

Fig. 2.8. Diagrammatic representation of the compression (continuous lines) and tension (interrupted lines) lamellae in a sagittal section of the upper end of right femur.

II. *Microscopically,* the bone is of four types, namely lamellar (including both compact and cancellous), fibrous; dentine and cement.

1. **Lamellar bone.** Most of the mature human bones, whether compact or cancellous, are composed of thin plates of bony tissue called lamellae. These are arranged in piles in a cancellous bone, but in concentric cylinders (Haversian system or secondary osteon) in a compact bone.

2. **Fibrous bone** is found in young foetal bones, but are common in reptiles and amphibia.

3. **Dentine** and

4. **Cement** occur in teeth.

GROSS STRUCTURE OF AN ADULT LONG BONE

Naked eye examination of the longitudinal and transverse sections of a long bone shows the following features :

1. **Shaft.** From without inwards, it is composed of periosteum, cortex and medullary cavity (Fig. 2.9). (a) *Periosteum* is a thick

fibrous membrane covering the surface of the bone. It is made up of an outer fibrous layer, and an inner cellular layer which is osteogenic in nature. Periosteum is united to the underlying bone by Sharpey's fibres, and the union is particularly strong over the attachments of tendons and ligaments. At the articular margin the periosteum is continuous with the capsule of the joint. The abundant periosteal arteries nourish the outer part of the under-lying cortex also. Periosteum has a rich nerve supply which makes it the most sensitive part of the bone. (b) *Cortex* is made up of a compact bone which gives it the desired strength to withstand all possible mechanical strains. (c) *Medullary cavity* is filled with red or yellow bone marrow. At birth the marrow is red everywhere with widespread active haemopoiesis. As the age advances the red marrow at many places atrophies and is replaced by yellow, fatty marrow, with no power of haemopoiesis. Red marrow persists in the cancellous ends of long bones. In the sternum ribs, vertebrae and skull bones the red marrow is found throughout life.

2. The **two ends** of a long bone are made up of cancellous bone covered with hyaline cartilage.

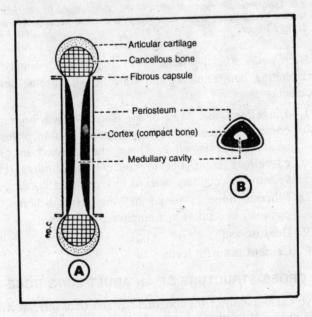

Fig. 2.9. Naked eye structure of an adult long bone.
(a) longitudinal section;
(b) transverse section of the shaft.

PARTS OF A YOUNG BONE

A typical long bone ossifies in three parts, the two ends from secondary centres, and the intervening shaft from a primary centre. Before ossification is complete the following parts of the bone can be defined (Fig. 2.10).

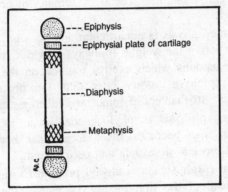

Fig. 2.10. Parts of a young long bone.

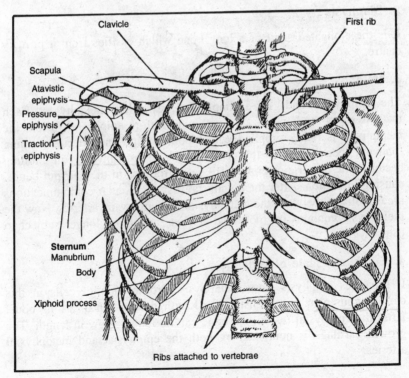

Fig. 2.11. Types of epiphyses and cartilages.

1. Epiphysis (Fig. 2.11)

The ends and tips of a bone which ossify from secondary centres are called epiphyses. These are of the following types :

(a) **Pressure epiphysis** is articular and takes part in transmission of the weight. Examples : head of femur; lower end of radius, etc.

(b) **Traction epiphysis** is nonarticular and does not take part in the transmission of the weight. It always provides attachment to one or more tendons which exert a traction on the epiphysis. The traction epiphyses ossify later than the pressure epiphyses. Examples : trochanters of femur and tubercles of humerus.

(c) **Atavistic epiphysis** is phylogenetically an independent bone which in man becomes fused to another bone. Examples : coracoid process of scapula and os trigonum.

(d) **Aberrant epiphysis** is not always present. Examples : epiphysis at the head of the first metacarpal and at the base of other metacarpal bones.

2. Diaphysis

It is the elongated shaft of a long bone which ossifies from a primary centre.

3. Metaphysis

The epiphysial ends of a diaphysis are called metaphyses. Each metaphysis is the zone of active growth. Before epiphysial fusion, the metaphysis is richly supplied with blood through end arteries forming 'hair-pin' bends. This is the common site of osteomyelitis in children because, the bacteria or emboli are easily trapped in the hair-pin bends, causing infraction. After the epiphysial fusion, vascular communications are established between the metaphysial and epiphysial arteries. Now the metaphysis contains no more end-arteries, and is no longer subject to osteomyelitis.

4. Epiphysial plate of cartilage

It separates epiphysis from metaphysis. Proliferation of cells in this cartilaginous plate is responsible for lengthwise growth of a long bone. After the epiphysial fusion, the bone can no longer grow in length. The growth cartilage is nourished by both the epiphysial and metaphysial arteries.

BLOOD SUPPLY OF BONES

1. Long Bones

The blood supply of a long bone is derived from the following sources (Fig. 2.12).

(a) **Nutrient artery** enters the shaft through the nutrient foramen, runs obliquely through the cortex, and divides into ascending and descending branches in the medullary cavity. Each branch divides into a number of small parallel channels which terminate in the adult metaphysis by anastomosing with the epiphysial, metaphysial and periosteal arteries. The nutrient artery supplies medullary cavity, inner 2/3 of cortex and metaphysis.

The *nutrient foramen* is directed away from the growing end of the bone; their directions are indicated by a jingle, 'To the elbow I go, from the knee I flee'. The details and variations in the diaphysial nutrient foramina are described by a number of authors (Ujwal, 1962; Mysorekar, 1967; Chhatrapati and Misra, 1967; Kate, 1971; Patake and Mysorekar, 1977; Mysorekar and Nandedkar, 1979; Longia et al., 1980).

The oblique direction of the nutrient foramina opposite to the growing end of the bone is best explained by the growing-end hypothesis. The alternative hypotheses such as 'periosteal slip theory', 'vascular theory' and 'asymmetrical muscular development theory' are reviewed by Kate (1971) and Patake and Mysorekar (1977).

(b) **Periosteal arteries** are especially numerous beneath the muscular and ligamentous attachments. They ramify beneath the periosteum and enter the Volkmann's canals to supply the outer 1/3 of the cortex.

(c) **Epiphysial arteries** are derived from periarticular vascular arcades (circulus vasculosus) found on the nonarticular bony surface. Out of the numerous vascular foramina in this region, only a few admit the arteries (epiphysial and metaphysial), and the rest are venous exits. The number and size of these foramina may give an idea of the relative vascularity of the two ends of a long bone (Tandon, 1964).

(d) **Metaphysial arteries** are derived from the neighbouring systemic vessels. They pass directly into the metaphysis and reinforce the metaphysial branches from the primary nutrient artery. For anatomical basis of osteomyelitis see under 'metaphysis'.

In miniature long bones, the infection begins in the middle of the shaft rather than at the metaphysis because, the nutrient artery breaks up into a plexus immediately upon reaching the medullary cavity. In the adults, however, the chances of infection are minimized because the nutrient artery is mostly replaced by the periosteal vessels.

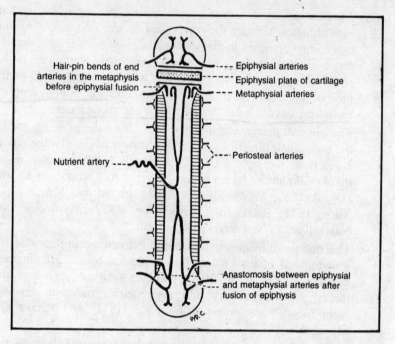

Hair-pin bends of end arteries in the metaphysis before epiphysial fusion

Epiphysial arteries
Epiphysial plate of cartilage
Metaphysial arteries

Nutrient artery

Periosteal arteries

Anastomosis between epiphysial and metaphysial arteries after fusion of epiphysis

Fig. 2.12. Blood supply of a long bone in which the upper epiphysis (growing end) has not yet fused with the diaphysis.

2. Other Bones

Short bones are supplied by numerous periosteal vessels which enter their nonarticular surfaces. In a vertebra, the body is supplied by anterior and posterior vessels, and the vertebral arch by large vessels entering the bases of transverse processes. Its marrow is drained by two large basivertebral veins. A rib is supplied by : (a) the nutrient artery which enters it just beyond the tubercle; and (b) the periosteal arteries.

Veins are numerous and large in the cancellous, red marrow bones (e.g., basivertebral veins). In the compact bone, they accompany arteries in the Volkmann's canals.

Lymphatics have not been demonstrated within the bone, although some of them do accompany the periosteal blood vessels, which drain to the regional lymph nodes.

NERVE SUPPLY OF BONES

Nerves accompany the blood vessels. Most of them are sympathetic and vasomotor in function. A few of them are sensory which are distributed to the articular ends and periosteum of the long bones, to the vertebra, and to large flat bones.

✕ DEVELOPMENT AND OSSIFICATION OF BONES

Bones are first laid down as mesodermal (connective tissue) condensations. Conversion of mesodermal models into bone is called *intramembranous* or *mesenchymal ossification*, and the bones are called membrane (dermal) bones.

However, mesodermal stage may pass through cartilaginous stage by chondrification during 2nd month of intrauterine life. Conversion of cartilaginous model into bone is called *intracartilaginous* or *endochondral ossification*, and such bones are called cartilaginous bones.

Ossification takes place by centres of ossification, each one of which is a point where lying down of lamellae (bone formation) starts by the osteoblasts situated on the newly formed capillary loops. The centres of ossification may be primary or secondary. The **primary centres** appear before birth, usually during 8th week of intrauterine life; the **secondary centres** appear after birth, with a few exceptions. Many secondary centres appear during puberty.

A primary centre forms diaphysis, and the secondary centres form epiphyses. Fusion of epiphyses with the diaphysis starts at puberty and is complete by the age of 25 years, after which no more bone growth can take place. The law of ossification states that secondary centres of ossification which appear first are last to unite. The end of a long bone where epiphysial fusion is delayed is called the growing end of the bone.

GROWTH OF A LONG BONE

1. Bone grows in length by multiplication of cells in the epiphysial plate of cartilage.
2. Bone grows in thickness by multiplication of cells in the periosteum.
3. Bones grow by deposition of new bone on the surface and at the ends. This process of bone deposition by osteoblasts is called appositional growth or surface accretion. However, in order to maintain the shape the unwanted bone must be removed. This process of bone removal by osteoblasts is called remodelling. This is how marrow cavity increases in size.

MEDICOLEGAL AND ANTHROPOLOGICAL ASPECTS

When a skeleton or isolated bones are received for medicolegal examination, one should be able to determine : (a) whether the bones are human or not; (b) whether they belong to one or more persons; (c) the age of the individual; (d) the sex; (e) the stature; and (f) the time and cause of death. For excellent details of all these points consult Modi (1977).

1. Estimation of Skeletal Age

Up to the age of 25 years, the skeletal age can be estimated to within 1-2 years of correct age by the states of dentition and ossification, provided the whole skeleton is available. From 25 years onwards, the skeletal age can be estimated to within ± 5 years of the correct age by the state of cranial sutures and of the bony surfaces of symphysis pubis.

In general, the appearance of secondary centres and fusion of epiphyses occur about one year earlier in females than in males. These events are also believed to occur 1-2 years (Bajaj et al., 1967) or 2-3 years (Pillai, 1936) earlier in India than in Western countries. However, Jit and Singh (1971) did not find any difference between the eastern and western races.

2. Estimation of Sex

Sex can be determined after the age of puberty. Sexual differences are best marked in the pelvis and skull, and accurate determination of sex can be done in over 90% cases with either pelvis or skull alone. However, sexual dimorphism has been worked out in a number of other bones, like sternum (Jit et al., 1980), atlas (Halim and Siddiqui, 1976), and most of the limb bones (see references at the end of the chapter).

3. Estimation of Stature (Height)

It is a common experience that trunk and limbs show characteristic ratios among themselves and in comparison with total height. Thus a number of regression formulae have been worked out to determine height from the length of the individual limb bones (Siddiqui and Shah, 1944; Singh and Sohal, 1952; Jit and Singh, 1956; Athawale, 1963; Kolte and Bansal, 1974; Kate and Majumdar, 1976). Height can also be determined from parts of certain long bones (Mysorekar et al., in press), from head length (Saxena et al., 1981), and from foot measurements (Charnalia, 1961; Qamra et al., 1980). CR length has been correlated with diaphysial length of foetal bones (Vare and Bansal, 1977) and with the neonatal and placental parameters (Jeyasingh et al., 1980; Saxena et al., 1981).

4. Estimation of Race

It is of interest to anthropologists. A number of metrical (like cranial and facial indices) and nonmetrical features of the skull, pelvis, and certain other bones are of racial significance (Krogman, 1962; Berry, 1975).

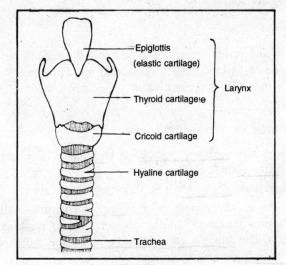

Fig. 2.13. Cartilages.

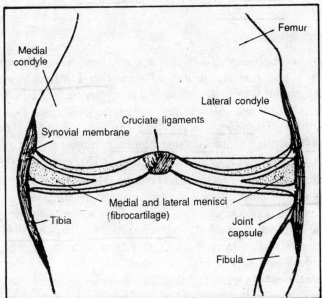

Knee joint — coronal (frontal) section

Fig. 2.14. Cartilage.

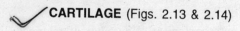

CARTILAGE (Figs. 2.13 & 2.14)

Synonyms

1. Chondros (G); 2. Gristle. Compare with the terms, chondrification, chondrodystrophy, synchondrosis, etc.

Definition

Cartilage is a connective tissue composed of cells (chondrocytes) and fibres (collagen or yellow elastic) embedded in a firm, gel-like matrix which is rich in a mucopolysaccharide. It is much more elastic than bone.

General Features

1. Cartilage has no blood vessels or lymphatics. The nutrition of cells diffuses through the matrix.
2. Cartilage has no nerves. It is, therefore, insensitive.
3. Cartilage is surrounded by a fibrous membrane, called perichondrium, which is similar to periosteum in structure and function. The articular cartilage has no perichondrium, so that its regeneration after injury is inadequate.
4. When cartilage calcifies, the chondrocytes die and the cartilage is replaced by bone.

Types of Cartilage

1. **Hyaline cartilage** (G. hyalos = transparent stone). It is bluish white and translucent due to very fine collagen fibres. Its distribution is most abundant, and has a tendency to calcify after 40 years of age. All cartilage bones are preformed in hyaline cartilage. Examples : embryonic cartilage, articular cartilage, costal cartilages, tracheal and bronchial cartilages, and most of the cartilages of nose and larynx (Fig. 2.15).
2. **Fibrocartilage.** It is white and opaque due to abundance of dense collagen fibres. Wherever fibrous tissue is subjected to great pressure, it is replaced by fibrocartilage which is tough, strong and resilient. Examples : intervertebral disc, intra-articular discs, menisci and labra. It lines certain bony grooves in which the tendons play (Fig. 2.16).
3. **Elastic cartilage.** It is made up of numerous cells and a rich network of yellow elastic fibres pervading the matrix, so that it is more pliable. Examples : cartilages in the external ear, auditory tube, and small cartilages at the inlet of larynx (Fig. 2.17).

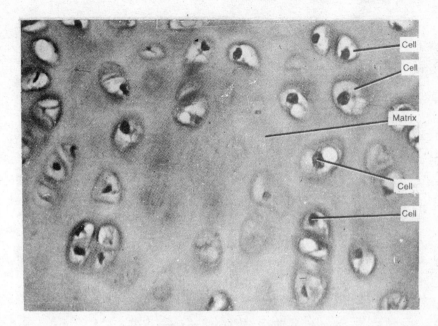

Fig. 2:15. Hyaline cartilage.

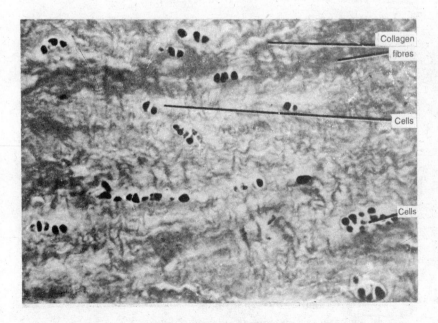

Fig. 2.16. Fibrocartilage.

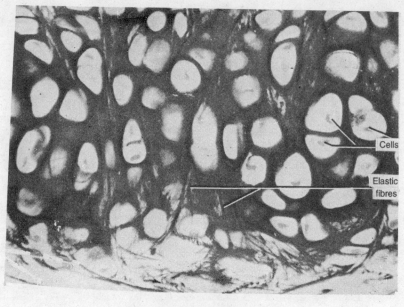

Fig. 2.17. Elastic cartilage.

APPLIED ANATOMY

1. Periosteum is particularly sensitive to tearing or tension. Drilling into the compact bone without anaesthesia causes only dull pain or an aching sensation; drilling into spongy bone is much more painful. Fractures, tumours and infections of the bone are very painful.

2. *Blood supply* of bone is so rich that it is very difficult to interrupt it sufficiently to kill the bone. Passing a metal pin into the medullary cavity hardly interferes with the blood supply of the bone.

3. **Fracture** is a break in the continuity of a bone. The fracture which is not connected with the skin wound is known as simple (closed) fracture; the fracture which communicates with the skin wound is known as compound (open) fracture. A fracture requires "reduction" by which the alignment of the broken ends is restored.

   Healing (repair) of a fracture takes place in three stages : (a) repair by granulation tissue; (b) union by callus; and (c) consolidation by mature bone.

4. In **rickets** (deficiency of vitamin D), calcification of cartilage fails and ossification of the growth zone is disturbed. Rickets affects the growing bones and, therefore, the disease develops

during the period of most rapid growth of skeleton, i.e., 3 months to 3 years. Osteoid tissue is formed normally and the cartilage cells proliferate freely, but mineralization does not take place. This results in craniotabes, rachitic rosary at the costochondral junctions, Harrison's sulcus at the diaphragmatic attachments, enlarged epiphyses in limb bones, and the spinal and pelvic deformities.

5. In scurvy (deficiency of vitamin C), formation of collageneous fibres and matrix is impaired. Defective formation of the inter-cellular cementing substances and lack of collagen cause rupture of capillaries and defective formation of new capillaries. Haema-tomata in the muscles and bones (subperiosteal) cause severe pain and tenderness. The normal architecture at the growing ends of the bones is lost.

6. Many skeletal defects are caused by genetic factors, or by a combination of genetic, hormonal, nutritional and pathological factors.

REFERENCES AND SUGGESTIONS FOR ADDITIONAL READING

Athawale, M.C. (1963). Estimation of height from lengths of forearm bones, a study of one hundred Maharashtrian male adults of ages between twenty five and thirty years. *Am. J. Phys. Anthropol.*, 21 : 105-112.

Bajaj, I.D., Bhardwaj, O.P. and Bhardwaj, S. (1967). Appearance and fusion of important ossification centres. A study of Delhi population. *Indian J. Med. Res.*, 55 : 1064-1067.

Berry, A.C. (1975). Factors affecting the incidence of non-metrical skeletal variants. *J. Anat.*, 120 : 519-535.

Brahma, K.C. and Mitra, N.L. (1973). Ossification of carpal bones. A radiological study in the tribals of Chotanagpur. *J. Anat. Soc. India*, 22 : 21-28.

Charnalia, V.M. (1961). Anthropological study of the foot and its relationship to stature in different castes and tribes of Pondicherry State. *J. Anat. Soc. India*, 10 : 26-30.

Chhatrapati, D.N. and Misra, B.D. (1967). Position of the nutrient foramen on the shafts of human long bones. *J. Anat. Soc. India*, 16 : 1-10.

Das Gupta, S.M., Prasad, V. and Singh, S. (1974). A roentgenologic study of epiphysial union around elbow, wrist and knee joints and the pelvis in boys and girls of Uttar Pradesh. *J. Indian Med. Assoc.*, 62 : 10-12.

Garg, K., Bahl, I., Mathur, R. and Verma, R.K. (1985). Bilateral asymmetry in surface area of carpal bones in children. J. Anat. Soc. Ind. 34 : 167-172.

Garg, K., Kulshrestha, V., Bahl, I., Mathur, R., Mittal, S.K. and Verma, R. (1988). Asymmetry in surface area of capitate and hamate bones in normal and malnourished children. J. Anat. Soc. Ind. 37 : 73-74.

Gupta, A., Garg, K., Mathur, R. and Mittal, S.K. (1988). Asymmetry in surface area of bony epiphysis of knee in normal and malnourished children. Ind. Paed. No. 10 : 999-1000.

Halim, A. and Siddiqui M.S. (1976). Sexing of atlas, *Indian J. Phys. Anthropol. Hum. Genet.*, 2 : 129-135.

Hasan, M. and Narayan, D. (1963). The ossification centres of carpal bones. A radiological study of the times of appearance in U.P. Indian subjects. *Indian J. Med. Res.*, 51 : 917-920.

Hasan, M. and Narayan, D. (1964). Radiological study of the postnatal ossification of the upper end of humerus in U.P. Indians. *J. Anat. Soc. India*, 13 : 70-75.

Jeyasingh, P., Saxena, S.K., Arora, A.K., Pandey, D.N. and Gupta, C.D. (1980). A study of correlations between some neonatal and placental parameters. *J. Anat. Soc. India*, 29 : 14-18.

Jit, I. (1957). Observations on prenatal ossification with special reference to the bones of hand and foot. *J. Anat. Soc. India*, 6 : 12-23.

Jit, I. (1972). Times of ossification in India (editorial). *Bull. PGI (Chandigarh)*, 6 : 100-103.

Jit, I. (1979). The house of skeletons case. *J. Anat. Soc. India*, 28 : 106-116.

Jit, I., Jhingan, V. and Kulkarni, M. (1980). Sexing of human sternum. *Am. J. Phys. Anthropol.*, 53 : 217-224.

Jit, I. and Gandhi, O P. (1966). The value of preauricular sulcus in sexing bony pelvis. *J. Anat. Soc. India*, 15 : 104-107.

Jit, I. and Kulkarni, M. (1976). Times of appearance and fusion of epiphysis at the medial end of the clavicle. *Indian J. Med. Res.*, 64 : 773-782.

Jit, I. and Singh, S. (1956). Estimation of the stature from the clavicle. *Indian J. Med. Res.*, 44 : 133-135.

Jit, I. and Singh S. (1966). Sexing of the adult clavicle. *Indian J. Med. Res.*, 54 : 551-571.

Jit, I. and Singh, B. (1971). A radiological study of the time of fusion of certain epiphyses in Punjabees. *J. Anat. Soc. India*, 20 : 1-27.

Jit, I., Verma, U. and Gandhi, O.P. (1968). Ossification of bones of the hand and foot in newborn children. *J. Anat. Soc. India*, 17 : 8-13.

Kate, B.R. (1964). A study of the regional variation of the Indian femur, the diameter of the head, its medicolegal and surgical application. *J. Anat. Soc. India*, 13 : 80-84.

Kate, B.R. (1967). The angle of the femoral neck in Indians. *East. Anthropologist*, 20 : 54-60.

Kate, B.R. (1971). Nutrient foramina in human long bones. *J. Anat. Soc. India*, 20 : 139-144.

Kate, B.R. and Majumdar, R.D. (1976). Stature estimation from femur and humerus by regression and autometry. *Acta Anat.*, 94 : 311-320.

Kolte, P.M. and Bansal, P.C. (1974). Determination of regression formulae for reconstruction of stature from the long bones of upper limb in Maharashtrians of Marathwada region. *J. Anat. Soc. India*, 23 : 6-11.

Krogman, W.M. (1962). *The Human Skeleton in Forensic Medicine*. Thomas, Springfield, Ill.

Longia, G.S., Ajmani, M.L., Saxena, S.K. and Thomas, R.J. (1980). Study of diaphysial nutrient foramina in the human long bones. *Acta Anat.*, 107 : 399-406.

Maniar, B.M., Seervai, M.H. and Kapur, P.L. (1974). A study of ossification centres in the hand and wrist of Indian children. *Indian Pediatr.*, 11 : 203-211.

Modi, N.J. (1977). *Modi's Textbook of Medical Jurisprudence and Toxicology*, 20th ed., p. 27-38, and 80-88, Tripathi, Bombay.

Mysorekar, V.R. (1967). Diaphysial nutrient foramina in human long bones. *J. Anat*, 101 : 813-822.

Mysorekar, V.R. and Nandedkar, A.N. (1979). Diaphysial nutrient foramina in human phalanges. *J. Anat.*, 128 : 315-322.

Mysorekar, V.R., Verma, P.K., Nandedkar, A.N. and Sarma, T.C.S.R. (1980). Estimation of stature from parts of bones, lower end of femur and upper end of radius. *Medicine Science and Law* (*Lond.*), 20 : 283-286.

Mysorekar, V.R., Nandedkar, A.N. and Sarma, T.C.S.R. (in press). Estimation of stature from parts of humerus and radius. *Medicine, Science and Law* (*Lond.*).

Narayan, D. and Bajaj, I.D. (1957). Ages of epiphysial union in long bones of inferior extremity in U.P. subjects. *Indian J. Med. Res.*, 45 : 645-649.

Patake, S.M. and Mysorekar, V.R. (1977). Diaphysial nutrient foramina in human metacarpals and metatarsals. *J. Anat.*, 124 : 299-304.

Pillai, M.J.S. (1936). The study of epiphysial union for determining the age of South Indians. *Indian J. Med. Res.*, 23 : 1015-1017.

Prakash, S., Chopra, S.R.K. and Jit, I. (1979). Ossification of the human patella. *J. Anat. Soc. India*, 28 : 78-83.

Qamra, S.R., Jit, I. and Deodhar, S.D. (1980). A model for reconstructing height from foot measurements in an adult population of north-west India. *Indian J. Med. Res.*, 71 : 77-83.

Raju, P.B. and Singh, S. (1978). Sexual dimorphism in scapula. *J. Indian Acad. Forens. Sci.*, 17 : 23-34.

Raju, B.P. and Singh, S. (1979). Sexual dimorphism in hip bone. *Indian J. Med. Res.*, 69 : 849-855.

Raju, P.B., Singh, S. and Padmanabhan, R. (1981). Sex determination and sacrum. *J. Anat. Soc. India*, 30 : 13-15.

Saxena, S.K., Jeyasingh, P., Gupta, A.K. and Gupta, C.D. (1981). Estimation of stature from measurement of head length. *J. Anat. Soc. India*, 30 : 78-79.

Saxena, S.K., Maewal, S., Pandey, D.N. and Gupta, C.D. (1981). A study of correlationships between CR length and neonatal and placental parameters. *J. Anat. Soc. India*, 30 : 67-69.

Siddiqui, M.A.H. and Shah, M.A. (1944). Estimation of stature from long bones of Punjabees. *Indian J. Med. Res.*, 32 : 105-108.

Singh, B. and Sohal, H.S. (1952). Estimation of stature from the length of clavicle in Punjabees, a preliminary report. *Indian J. Med. Res.*, 40 : 67-71.

Singh, G., Singh, S. (1976). Identification of sex from the fibula. *J. Indian Acad. Forens. Sci.*, 15 : 29-34.

Singh G., Singh, S.P. and Singh, S. (1974). Identification of sex from the radius. *J. Indian Acad. Forens. Sci.*, 13 : 10-16.

Singh, G., Singh, S. and Singh, S.P. (1975). Identification of sex from tibia. *J. Anat. Soc. India*, 24 : 20-24.

Singh, I. (1978). The architecture of cancellous bone. *J. Anat.*, 127 : 305-310.

Singh, S. and Gangrade, K.C. (1968). The sexing of adult clavicles. Demarking points for Varanasi zone. *J. Anat. Soc. India*, 17 : 89-100.

Singh S. and Potturi, B.R. (1978). Greater sciatic notch in sex determination. *J. Anat.*, 127 : 619-624.

Singh, S. and Raju, P.B. (1977). Identification of sex from the hip bone, demarking points. *J. Anat. Soc. India*, 26 : 111-117.

Singh, S. and Singh, S.P. (1972). Identification of sex from the humerus. *Indian J. Med. Res.*, 60 : 1061-1066.

Singh, S. and Singh, S.P. (1974). Weight of the femur, a useful measurement for identification of sex. *Acta Anat.*, 87 : 141-145.

Singh, S. and Singh, S.P. (1975). Identification of sex from tarsal bones. *Acta Anat.*, 93 : 568-573.

Singh S., Singh, G. and Singh, S.P. (1974). Identification of sex from the ulna. *Indian J. Med. Res.*, 62 : 731-735.

Singh S.P. and Singh, S. (1972 a). The sexing of adult femora, demarking points for Varanasi zone. *J. Indian Acad. Forens. Sci.*, 11 : 1-6.

Singh S.P. and Singh, S. (1972 b). Identification of sex from the head of a femur, the demarking points of Varanasi zone. *Indian Med. Gaz.*, 12 : 45-49.

Srivastava, K.K., Pai, R.A., Kolbhandari, M.P. and Kant, K. (1971). Cleidocranial dysostosis : A clinical and cytological study. *Clin. Genet.*, 2 : 104-110.

Tandon, B.K. (1964). A study of the vascular foramina at the two ends of ulna. *J. Anat. Soc. India*, 13 : 24-27.

Ujwal, Z.S. (1962). Nutrient canal of long bones. *Univ. Rajasthan Studies*, 6 : 39-43.

Vare, A.M. and Bansal, P.C. 1977). Estimation of crown-rump length from diaphysial lengths of foetal long bones. *J. Anat. Soc. India*, 26 : 91-93.

3

Joints

Related Terms

1. Arthron (G. a joint). Compare with the terms arthrology, synarthrosis, diarthrosis, arthritis, arthrodesis, etc.
2. Articulatio (L. a joint); articulation (NA).
3. Junctura (L. a joint).
4. Syndesmology (G. syndesmos = ligament) is the study of ligaments and related joints.

Definition

Joint is a junction between two or more bones or cartilages. It is a device to permit movements. However, immovable joints are primarily meant for growth, and may permit moulding during childbirth.

There are more joints in a child than in an adult because as growth proceeds some of the bones fuse together — e.g. the ilium, ischium and pubis to form the pelvic bone; the two halves of the infant frontal bone, and of the infant mandible; the five sacral vertebrae and the four coccygeal vertebrae.

CLASSIFICATION OF JOINTS

A. Structural Classification (Fig. 3.1)

1. **Fibrous joints :** (a) Sutures; (b) syndesmosis; and (c) gomphosis.
2. **Cartilaginous joints :** (a) Primary cartilaginous joints or synchondrosis; and (b) secondary cartilaginous joints or symphysis.
3. **Synovial joints :** (a) Ball-and-socket or spheroidal joints; (b) Sellar or saddle joints; (c) condylar or bicondylar joints; (d) ellipsoid joints; (e) hinge joints; (f) pivot or trochoid joints and (g) plane joints.

B. Functional Classification (According to the degree of mobility)

1. **Synarthrosis** (immovable), like fibrous joints.

2. **Amphiarthrosis** (slightly movable), like cartilaginous joints.
3. **Diarthrosis** (freely movable), like synovial joints.

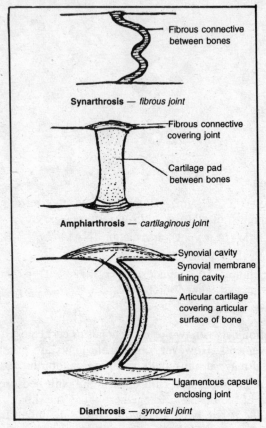

Fig. 3.1. Types of joints.

<u>Synarthroses</u> are fixed joints at which there is no movement. The articular surfaces are joined by tough fibrous tissue. Often the edges of the bones are dovetailed into one another as in the sutures of the skull.

<u>Amphiarthroses</u> are joints at which slight movement is possible. A pad of cartilage lies between the bone surfaces, and there is a fibrous capsule to hold the bones and cartilage in place. The cartilages of such joints also act as shock absorbers, e.g. the intervertebral discs between the bodies of the vertebrae, where the cartilage is strengthened by extra collagen fibres.

<u>Diarthroses</u> or **synovial joints** are known as freely movable joints, though at some of them the movement is restricted by the shape of the articulating surfaces and by the ligaments which hold the bones together. These ligaments are of elastic connective tissue.

A synovial joint has a fluid-filled cavity between articular surfaces which are covered by articular cartilage. The fluid, known as synovial fluid, is a form of lymph produced by the synovial membrane which lines the cavity except for the actual articular surfaces and covers any ligaments or tendons which pass through the joint. Synovial fluid acts as a lubricant.

The form of the articulating surfaces controls the type of movement which takes place at any joint.

The movements possible at synovial joints are :

Angular	flexion : decreasing the angle between two bones;
	extension : increasing the angle between two bones;
	abduction : moving the part away from the mid-line;
	adduction : bringing the part towards the mid-line.
Rotary	rotation : turning upon an axis;
	circumduction : moving the extremity of the part round in a circle so that the whole part inscribes a cone.
Gliding	one part slides on another.

C. Regional Classification

1. **Skull type :** immovable.
2. **Vertebral type :** slightly movable.
3. **Limb type :** freely movable.

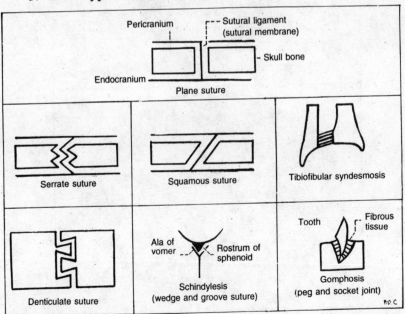

Fig. 3.2. Types of fibrous joints.

The structural classification is most commonly followed, and will be considered in detail in the following paragraphs.

FIBROUS JOINTS (Fig. 3.2)

In fibrous joints the bones are joined by fibrous tissue. These joints are either immovable or permit a slight degree of movement. These can be grouped in the following three subtypes.

1. **Sutures.** These are peculiar to skull, and are immovable. According to the shape of bony margins, the sutures can be plane, serrate, denticulate, squamous, limbous, and of schindylesis type (Fig. 3.3).

2. **Syndesmosis.** The bones are connected by the interosseous ligament. Example : inferior tibiofibular joint.

3. **Gomphosis** (peg and socket joint). Example : tooth in its socket.

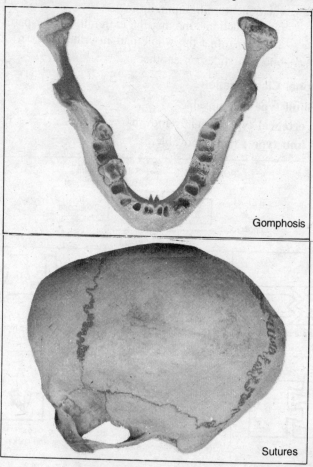

Gomphosis

Sutures

Fig. 3.3. Fibrous joints.

✓ CARTILAGINOUS JOINTS

In this type of joints the bones are joined by cartilage. These are of the following two types (Fig. 3.4).

1. **Primary cartilaginous joints (synchondrosis, or hyaline cartilage joints).** The bones are united by a plate of hyaline cartilage, so that the joint is immovable and strong. These joints are temporary in nature because after a certain age the cartilaginous plate is replaced by bone (synostosis). Examples : (a) joint between epiphysis and diaphysis of a growing long bone; (b) spheno-occipital joint; (c) first chondrosternal joint; and (d) costochondral joints.

2. **Secondary cartilaginous joints (symphyses or fibrocartilaginous joints).** The articular surfaces are covered by a thin layer of hyaline cartilage, and united by a disc of fibrocartilage. These joints are permanent and persist throughout life. In this respect symphysis menti is a misnomer. Typically the secondary cartilaginous joints occur in the median plane of the body, and permit limited movements due to compressible pad of fibro-cartilage and the occasional fluid filled cavities, such as in the pubic and manubriosternal joints; the thickness of fibrocartilage is directly related to the range of movement. Secondary cartilaginous joints may represent an intermediate stage in the evolution of synovial joints. Examples : (a) symphysis pubis; (b) manubriosternal joint; and (c) intervertebral joints between the vertebral bodies.

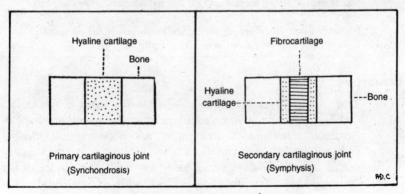

Fig. 3.4. Types of cartilaginous joints.

✓ SYNOVIAL JOINTS (Fig. 3.5)

Synovial joints are most evolved, and, therefore, most mobile type of joints.

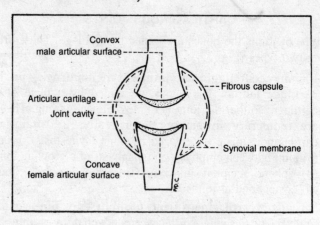

Fig. 3.5. Structure of a synovial joint.

Classification of Synovial Joints and their Movements

Type of Joint	Movements
A. Plane or gliding type	Gliding movement
B. Uniaxial joints	
1. Hinge joint	Flexion and extension
2. Pivot joint	Rotation only
C. Biaxial joints	
1. Condylar joint	Flexion and extension, and limited rotation
2. Ellipsoid joint	Flexion, extension, abduction, adduction, and circumduction
D. Multiaxial joints	
1. Saddle joint	Flexion and extension, abduction, adduction, and conjunct rotation
2. Ball-and-socket (spheroidal) joint	Flexion and extension, abduction and adduction, circumduction, and rotation

Characters

1. The articular surfaces are covered with hyaline (articular) cartilage (occasionally fibrocartilage in certain membrane bones). *Articular cartilage* is avascular, non-nervous and elastic. Lubricated with synovial fluid, the cartilage provides slippery surfaces for free movements, like 'ice on ice'. The surface of the cartilage shows fine undulations filled with synovial fluid.

2. Between the articular surfaces there is a *joint cavity* filled with synovial fluid. The cavity may be partially or completely subdivided by an articular disc or meniscus.

3. The joint is surrounded by an *articular capsule* which is made up of a fibrous capsule lined by synovial membrane. Because of its rich nerve supply, the *fibrous capsule* is sensitive to stretches

imposed by movements. This sets up appropriate reflexes to protect the joint from any sprain. This is called the 'watch-dog' action of the capsule. The fibrous capsule is often reinforced by : (a) *capsular* or *true ligaments* representing thickenings of the fibrous capsule; and (b) the *accessory ligaments* (distinct from fibrous capsule) which may be intra or extracapsular.

The *synovial membrane* lines whole of the interior of the joint, except for the articular surfaces covered by hyaline cartilage. The membrane secretes a slimy viscous fluid called the synovia or

FEATURES OF DIFFERENT SYNOVIAL JOINTS (Figs. 3.6 & 3.7)

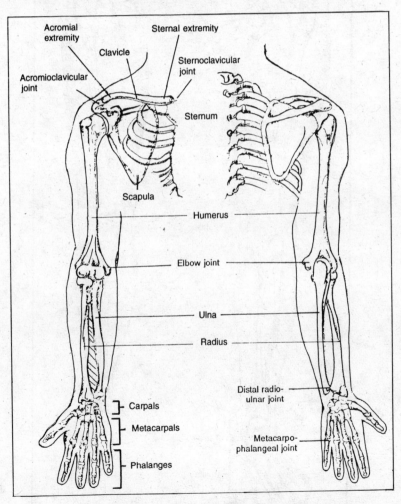

Fig. 3.6. Bones and joints of upper limb.

synovial fluid which lubricates the joint and nourishes the articular cartilage. The viscosity of fluid is due to hyaluronic acid secreted by cells of the synovial membrane.

4. Varying degrees of movements are always permitted by the synovial joints.

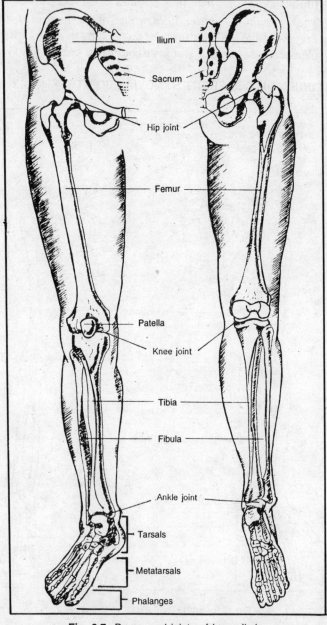

Fig. 3.7. Bones and joints of lower limb.

1. Plane Synovial Joints

Articular surfaces are more or less flat (plane). They permit gliding movements (translations) in various directions. Examples : (a) intercarpal joints; (b) intertarsal joints; (c) joints between articular processes of vertebrae, etc. (Fig. 3.8).

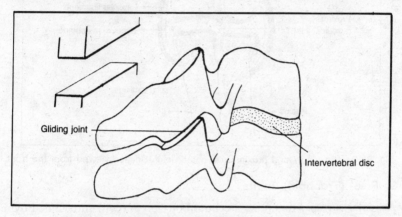

Fig. 3.8. Plane or gliding joint.

2. Hinge Joints (Ginglymi)

Articular surfaces are pulley-shaped. There are strong collateral ligaments. Movements are permitted in one plane around a transverse axis. Examples : (a) elbow joint (b) ankle joint; and (c) interphalangeal joints (Figs. 3.9 & 3.10).

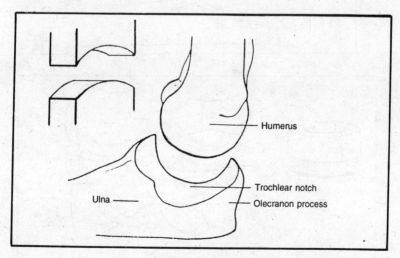

Fig. 3.9. Hinge joint.

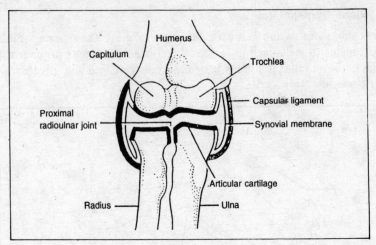

Fig. 3.10. The elbow and proximal radioulnar joint. Section viewed from the front.

3. Pivot (Trochoid) Joints

Articular surfaces comprise a central bony pivot (peg) surrounded by an osteoligamentous ring. Movements are permitted in one plane around a vertical axis. Examples : (a) superior and inferior radio-ulnar joints; and (b) median atlanto-axial joint (Figs. 3.11 & 3.12).

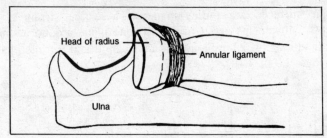

Fig. 3.11.

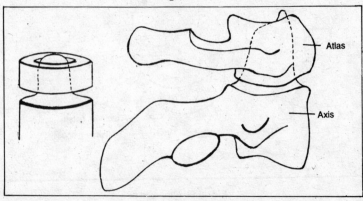

Fig. 3.12. Pivot joint.

4. Condylar (Bicondylar) Joints

Articular surfaces include two distinct condyles (convex **male** surfaces) fitting into reciprocally concave female surfaces (which are also, sometimes, known as condyles, such as in tibia). These joints permit movements mainly in one plane around a transverse axis, but partly in another plane (rotation) around a vertical axis. Examples : (a) knee joint (Figs. 3.13 & 3.14); and (b) right and left jaw joints.

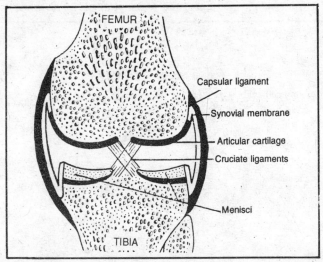

Fig. 3.13. Knee joint.

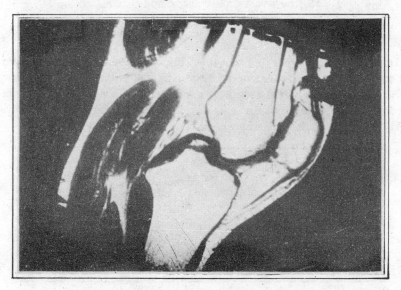

Fig. 3.14. Nuclear magnetic resonance scan of knee joint.

5. Ellipsoid Joints

Articular surfaces include an oval, convex, male surface fitting into an elliptical, concave female surface. Free movements are permitted around both the axes, flexion and extension around the transverse axis, and abduction and adduction around the anteroposterior axis. Combination of movements produces circumduction. Typical rotation around a third (vertical) axis does not occur. Examples : (a) wrist joint (Fig. 3.15); (b) metacarpophalangeal joints; and (c) atlanto-occipital joints.

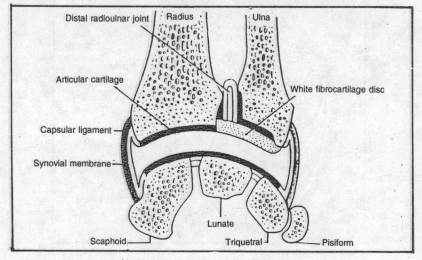

Fig. 3.15. The wrist and distal radioulnar joints. Anterior view.

6. Saddle (Sellar) Joints

Articular surfaces are reciprocally concavoconvex. Movements are similar to those permitted by an ellipsoid joint, with addition of some rotation (conjunct rotation) around a third axis which, however, cannot occur independently. Examples : (a) first carpometacarpal joint (Fig. 3.16); (b) sternoclavicular joint; and (c) calcaneocuboid joint.

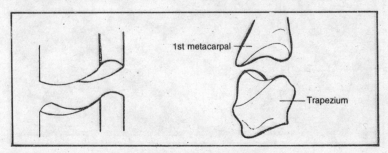

Fig. 3.16. Saddle joint.

7. Ball-and-Socket (Spheroidal) Joints

Articular surfaces include a globular head (male surface) fitting into a cup-shaped socket (female surface). Movements occur around an indefinite number of axes which have one common centre. Flexion, extension, abduction, adduction, medial rotation, lateral rotation, and circumduction, all occur quite freely. Examples :

(a)   shoulder joint;

(b)   hip joint (Fig. 3.17);

(c)   talo-calcaneonavicular joint.

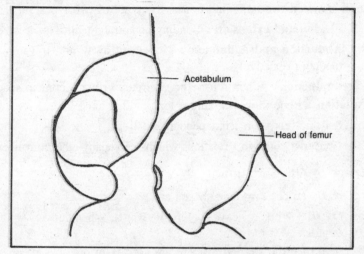

Fig. 3.17. Ball and socket joint.

CLASSIFICATION AND MOVEMENTS OF SYNOVIAL JOINTS

1. Terminology and Definition

Human Kinesiology : Study of geometry of surfaces and their associated movements.

Male surface : An articulating surface which is larger in surface area and always convex in all directions.

Female surface : An articulating surface which is smaller and concave in all directions.

Simple joints : Joints with only two articulating surfaces, i.e., male and female.

Compound joints : Joint possessing more than one pair of articulating surfaces.

Degrees of freedom : Number of axes at which the bone in a joint can move.

Uni-axial : Movement of bone at a joint is limited to one axis, i.e., with one degree of freedom.

Biaxial : With two degrees of freedom.

Multi-axial : Three axes along with intermediate positions also.

Translation : Sliding movements of one articulating surface over the other.

2. Movements and Mechanism of Joints

Angular movement : Movement leading to diminution or increase in angle between two adjoining bones. They are of two types :

(a) **Flexion and extension** : Bending and straightening respectively.

(b) **Abduction and adduction** : Movement away and towards the median respectively.

Circumduction : When a long bone circumscribes a conical space.

Rotation : Bone moves around a longitudinal axis.

(a) **Adjunct rotation** : independent rotations.

(b) **Conjunct rotation** : rotations which accompany other movements.

3. Shape of Articular Surface

The common articular surface shapes are :

(a) **Ovoid** : When concave — female ovoids. When convex — male ovoids.

(b) **Sellar/saddle shaped** : These are convex in one plane, concave in the perpendicular plane.

4. Mechanical Axis of a Bone and Movement of a Bone

It is a reference point around which joint mechanics can be studied and around which the most habitual conjunct rotation occurs.

Spin : Simple rotation around the bone's stationary mechanical axis.

Swing : Any other displacement of the bone and its mechanical axis apart from spin is termed a swing.

Swing may be pure or impure (swing + element of spin).

Ovoid of motion : This represents the imaginary surface which would include all possible paths of a point on the mechanical axis at some distance from its related joint.

Cardinal swing : When the mechanical axis moves in the shortest pathway when bone moves.

Arcuate swing : When the mechanical axis moves in the longest pathway along with the bony movement.

Co-spin : When the effect of adjunct rotation is additive to the rotation.

Anti-spin : Adjunct rotation which has a nullifying effect on rotation.

Joint Positions

Close packed position : When the joint surfaces become completely congruent, their area of contact is maximal and they are tightly compressed.

In this position fibrous capsule and ligaments are maximally spiralized and tense; no further movement is possible; surfaces cannot be separated by disruptive forces; articular surfaces are liable to trauma, e.g., shoulder — abduction + lateral rotation; hip — extension + medial rotation; knee — full extension; ankle — dorsiflexion.

Loose packed : All other positions of incongruency, e.g., least packed position. Sh. — semiabduction; hip — semiflexion; knee — semiflexion; ankle — ventral position.

Limitation of Movement

Factors

- Reflex contraction of antagonistic muscles;
- Due to stimulations of mechanoreceptors in articular tissue;
- Ligaments tension;
- Approximation of soft parts.

MECHANISM OF LUBRICATION OF A SYNOVIAL JOINT

1. **Synovial fluid**, secreted by synovial membrane, is sticky and viscous due to hyaluronic acid (a mucopolysaccharide). It serves the main function of lubrication of the joint, but also nourishes the articular cartilage.

2. **Hyaline cartilage** covering the articular surfaces possesses inherent slipperiness, like that of the ice.

3. **Intra-articular fibrocartilages**, articular discs or menisci, complete or incomplete, help in spreading the synovial fluid throughout the joint cavity, but particularly between the articular surfaces.

4. **Haversian fatty pads** (Haversian glands) occupy extra spaces in the joint cavity between the incongruous bony surfaces. All of them are covered with synovial membrane, and perhaps function as swabs to spread the synovial fluid.

BLOOD SUPPLY OF SYNOVIAL JOINTS

The articular and epiphysial branches given off by the neighbouring arteries form a periarticular arterial plexus. Numerous vessels from this plexus pierce the fibrous capsule and form a rich vascular plexus in the deeper parts of synovial membrane. The blood vessels of the synovial membrane terminate around the articular margins in a fringe of looped anastomoses termed the circulus vasculosus (*circulus articularis vasculosus*). It supplies capsule, synovial membrane, and the epiphysis. The articular cartilage is avascular.

After epiphysial fusion, communications between circulus vasculosus and the end arteries of metaphysis are established, thus minimizing the chances of osteomyelitis in the metaphysis.

NERVE SUPPLY OF SYNOVIAL JOINTS

1. The *capsule* and *ligaments* possess a rich nerve supply, which makes them acutely sensitive to pain. The synovial membrane has a poor nerve supply and is relatively insensitive to pain. The articular cartilage is non-nervous and totally insensitive.

   Articular nerves contain sensory and autonomic fibres. Some of the sensory fibres are proprioceptive in nature; these are sensitive to position and movement, and are concerned with the reflex control of posture and locomotion. Other sensory fibres are sensitive to pain. Autonomic fibres are vasomotor or vasosensory.

   The joint pain is often diffuse, and may be associated with nausea, vomiting, slowing of pulse, and fall in blood pressure. The pain commonly causes reflex contraction of muscles which fix the joint in a position of maximum comfort. Like visceral pain, the joint pain is also referred to uninvolved joints.

2. The principles of distribution of nerves to joints were first described by Hilton (1891). Hilton's law states that a motor nerve to the muscle acting on joint tends to give a branch to that joint (capsule) and another branch to the skin covering the joint.

   The concept of innervation of a joint was further elucidated by Gardner (1948) who observed that each nerve innervates a specific region of the capsule, and that the part of the capsule which is rendered taut by a given muscle is innervated by the nerve supplying its antagonists. Thus the pattern of innervation is concerned with the maintenance of an efficient stability at the joint.

LYMPHATIC DRAINAGE OF SYNOVIAL JOINTS

Lymphatics form a plexus in the subintima of the synovial membrane, and drain along the blood vessels to the regional deep nodes.

STABILITY OF SYNOVIAL JOINTS

The various factors maintaining stability at a joint are described below in order of their importance.

1. **Muscles.** The tone of different groups of muscles acting on the joint is the most important and indispensable factor in maintaining the stability. Without muscles, the knee and shoulder would be unstable, and arches of the foot would collapse.

2. **Ligaments** are important in preventing any over-movement, and in guarding against sudden accidental stresses. However, they do not help against a continuous strain, because once stretched, they tend to remain elongated. In this respect the elastic ligaments (ligamenta flava and ligaments of the joints of auditory ossicles) are superior to the common type of white fibrous ligaments.

3. **Bones** help in maintaining stability only in firm type of joints, like the hip and ankle. Otherwise in most of the joints (shoulder, knee, sacroiliac, etc.) their role is negligible.

APPLIED ANATOMY

1. **Dislocation of joint.** This is a condition in which the articular surfaces of the joint are abnormally displaced; so that one surface loses its contact completely from the other. If a partial contact is still retained, it is better called subluxation. Dislocation is commonly caused by trauma, and is characterized by pain, deformity, and loss of function. X-ray is confirmatory.

2. **Sprain** is the severe pain in a joint caused by ligamentous tear, but without any associated dislocation or fracture. The tear leads to effusion into the ligament and joint causing great pain.

3. **Arthritis** is inflammation of one or more joints. It can be caused by a variety of diseases, but the common types of arthritis are rheumatic, rheumatoid, osteoarthritis, and tuberculous. The involved joint is commonly swollen, and its movements are restricted and painful.

   Osteoarthritis represents the ageing process. In old age, the articular cartilage shows degenerative change in the centre (*fibrillation of cartilage*), and proliferative change around the edges (*osteophytes*). Lipping of the joint means formation of lips at the edges.

4. **Stiffness of joints related to weather.** The viscosity of synovial fluid increases with fall in temperature. This accounts for stiffness of the joints in cold weather. Mobility of joint in itself is an

important factor in promoting lubrication. Thus the stiffness of joints experienced in the morning gradually passes off as the movements are resumed.

5. **Neuropathic joint** is the result of its complete denervation, so that all reflexes are eliminated and the joint is left unprotected and liable to mechanical damage. A neuropathic joint shows painless swelling, excessive mobility and bony destruction. It is commonly caused by leprosy, tabes dorsalis and syringomyelia.

REFERENCES AND SUGGESTIONS FOR ADDITIONAL READING

Barnett, C.H., Davies, D.V. and MacConail, M.A. (1961). *Synovial Joints : Their Structure and Mechanics.* Longmans, London.

Freeman, M.A.R. (1973). *Adult Articular Cartilage* (editor). Pitman Medical, London.

Gardner, E.D. (1948). The innervation of the knee joint. *Anat. Rec.,* 101 : 109-131; The innervation of the shoulder joint. *Anat. Rec.,* 102 : 1-18, 1948.

Hilton, J. (1891). *Rest and Pain* edited by W.H.A. Jacobson and reprinted from the last London edition, P.W. Garfield, Cincinnati.

Kapandji, I.A. (1970). *The Physiology of the Joints.* Livingstone, London.

Kellgren, J.H. and Samual, E.P. (1950). Sensitivity and innervation of the articular capsule. *J. Bone Jt. Surg.,* 32b : 84-92.

MacConail, M.A. (1932). The function of intra-articular fibrocartilages, with special reference to the knee and inferior radio-ulnar joints. *J. Anat.,* 66 : 210-227.

MacConail, M.A. and Basmajian, J.V. (1977). *Muscles and Movements.* Krieger Publishing Company, New York.

Steindler, A. (1955). *Kinesiology of the Human Body.* Thomas, Springfield, Ill.

4

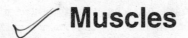
Muscles

Derivation of Name

Muscles (L. Mus = mouse) are so named because, many of them resemble a mouse, with their tendons representing the tail.

Definition

Muscle is a contractile tissue which brings about movements. Muscles can be regarded as motors of the body.

Types of Muscles

The muscles are of three types, skeletal, smooth and cardiac. The characters of each type are summarized below.

A. Skeletal Muscles (Striped, Striated, Somatic, or Voluntary Muscles)

1. These muscles are most abundant, found attached to skeleton;
2. exhibit cross-striations under microscope, and are considered to be the best differentiated form of muscle;
3. are supplied by somatic (cerebrospinal) nerves, and, therefore, are under voluntary control, with certain exceptions;
4. respond quickly to stimuli, being capable of rapid contractions, and, therefore, get fatigued easily;
5. help in adjusting the individual to external environment;
6. are under highest nervous control of cerebral cortex; and
7. each muscle fibre is a multinucleated cylindrical cell, containing groups of myofibrils (Cohnheim's areas) which, in turn, are made up of myofilaments of three types (myosin, actin and tropomyosin), the actual contractile elements.

   Examples : Muscles of limbs and body wall, and branchial muscles.

B. Smooth Muscles (Plain, Unstriped, Non-striated, Visceral, or Involuntary Muscles)

1. These muscles often encircle or surround the viscera;
2. do not exhibit cross-striations under microscope, being plain and smooth in form;
3. are supplied by autonomic nerves, and, therefore, are not under voluntary control;
4. respond slowly to stimuli, being capable of sustained contraction, and, therefore, do not fatigue easily;
5. provide motor power for regulating the internal environment, related to digestion, circulation, secretion and excretion;
6. are less dependent on nervous control, being capable of contracting automatically, spontaneously, and often rhythmically; and
7. each muscle fibre is an elongated, spindle-shaped cell, with a single nucleus placed centrally; the myofibrils show longitudinal striations.

Examples : Muscles of the blood vessels, and the arrector pili muscles of the skin.

C. Cardiac Muscle

1. It forms myocardium of the heart;
2. it is intermediate in structure, being striated and at the same time involuntary;
3. it is meant for automatic and rhythmic-contractions; and
4. each muscle fibre, having a single nucleus placed centrally, branches and anastomoses with the neighbouring fibres at inter-calated discs (apposed cell membranes); the cross-striations are less prominent than those in the skeletal muscle.

D. Myoepithelial Cells

These are present at the bases of secretary acini of sweat gland, etc. These help in expulsion of secretion from the acini.

Out of the four kinds of muscles, the skeletal muscles are most abundant in the body. These are the only muscles which are dissected out in the dissection hall and studied individually. Their details are given below.

SKELETAL MUSCLES (Fig. 4.2)

Synonyms

1. striped muscles; 2. striated muscles; 3. somatic muscles; 4. voluntary muscles.

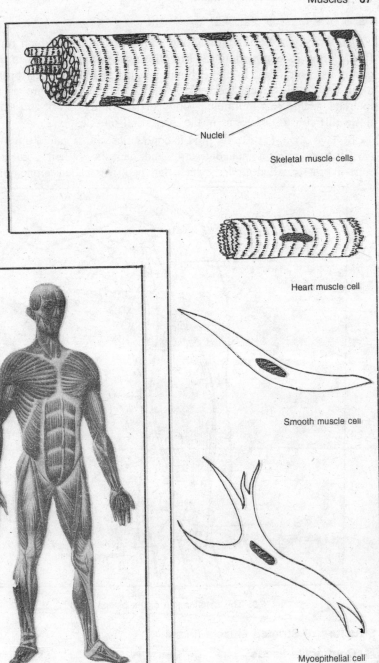

Nuclei

Skeletal muscle cells

Heart muscle cell

Smooth muscle cell

Myoepithelial cell

Fig. 4.2. Skeletal muscles.

Fig. 4.1. Various muscle cells.

Parts of a Muscle (Fig. 4.3)

A. Two ends. (1) **Origin** is one end of the muscle which remains fixed during its contraction. (2) **Insertion** is the other end which moves during its contraction. In the limb muscles, the origin is usually proximal to insertion. However, the terms, origin and insertion, are at times interchangeable (e.g., climbing action of latissimus dorsi), and at other times difficult to define, as in the intercostal muscles.

B. Two parts. (1) **Fleshy part** is contractile, and is called the 'belly'. (2) **Fibrous part** is noncontractile and inelastic. When cord-like or rope-like, it is called tendon; when flattened, it is called aponeurosis.

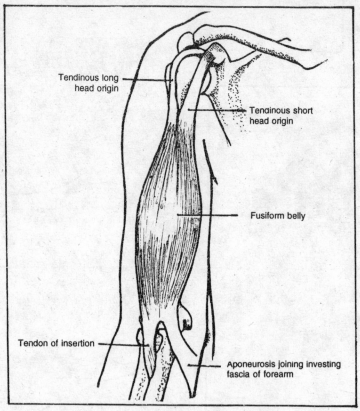

Tendinous long head origin

Tendinous short head origin

Fusiform belly

Tendon of insertion

Aponeurosis joining investing fascia of forearm

Fig. 4.3. The construction of the biceps brachii.

Structure of Striated Muscle (Fig. 4.4)

A. Contractile tissue

Each muscle is composed of numerous muscle fibres (Fig. 4.4A). Each **muscle fibre** is a multinucleated, cross-striated cylindrical cell (myocyte) 1-300 mm long. It is made up of a sarcolemma (cell membrane) enclosing sarcoplasm (cytoplasm). Embedded in the sarcoplasm there are (a) several hundreds of nuclei arranged at the periphery beneath the sarcolemma and (b) a number of evenly distributed longitudinal threads called **myofibrils** (Fig. 4.4B). Each myofibril (Fig. 4.4C) shows alternate dark and light bands. Dark bands are known as A bands (anisotropic) and the light bands as I bands (isotropic). The bands of adjacent fibrils are aligned transversely, so that the muscle fibre appears cross-striated. In the middle of A band there is a light H band with M band (dark) in its middle. In the middle of I band there is a dark Z disc or Krauses membrane. The segment of myofibril between two Z discs is called sarcomere.

Each myofibril is composed of longitudinal protein filaments, called **myofilaments**, which are the actual contractile elements of the striated muscle. Myofilaments are of two types, the thin **actin filaments**, and the thick **myosin filaments** (Fig. 4.4D). During muscular contraction, the actin filaments slide between the myosin filaments towards the centre of the sarcomere, thus bringing the attached Z discs closer together, with shortening of the contractile unit.

B. Supporting tissue

It helps in organization of the muscle. *Endomysium* surrounds each muscle fibre separately. *Perimysium* surrounds bundles (fasciculi or myonemes) of muscle fibres of various sizes. *Epimysium* surrounds the entire muscle. The connective tissue of the muscle becomes continuous with the tendon.

Slow and Fast Muscle Fibres (Dubowitz, 1969; Gauthier & Schaeffer, 1974)

1. **Type I (slow) fibres** show a slow 'tonic' contraction characteristic of postural muscles. These are red in colour because of large amounts of myoglobin. The fibres are rich in mitochondria and oxidative enzymes, but poor in phosphorylases. Because of a well-developed aerobic metabolism, slow fibres are highly resistant to fatigue.

2. **Type II (fast) fibres** show a fast 'phasic' contraction required for large-scale movements of body segments. These are paler (white) in colour because of small amounts of myoglobin. The fibres are rich in glycogen and phosphorylases, but poor in mitochondria and oxidative enzymes. Because of a glycolytic respiration, the fast fibres are quite easily fatigued.

3. **Intermediate fibres** represent a variant of type II (fast) fibres which are relatively resistant to fatigue, although less than type I (slow) fibres (Burke et al., 1973).

The three types of muscle fibres correspond to the different types of motor units found in mammals.

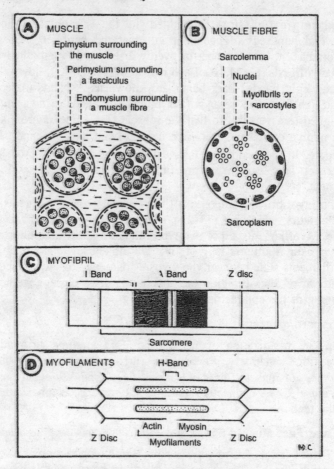

Fig. 4.4. Structure of the skeletal muscle. (A) Organization of muscle by connective tissue. (B) Transverse section of a muscle fibre. (C) Structure of a myofibril. The central line in A-band represents the H-band. (D) Arrangement of myofilaments in a myofibril.

In man, most of the skeletal muscles show a mixture of fibre types, but any one type may predominate.

Fascicular Architecture of Muscles (Fig. 4.5)

The arrangement of muscle fibres varies according to the direction, force and range of habitual movement at a particular joint. The force of movement is directly proportional to the number and size of muscle fibres, and the range of movement is proportional to the length of fibres. The muscles can be classified according to the arrangement of their fasciculi into the following groups (Fig. 4.5).

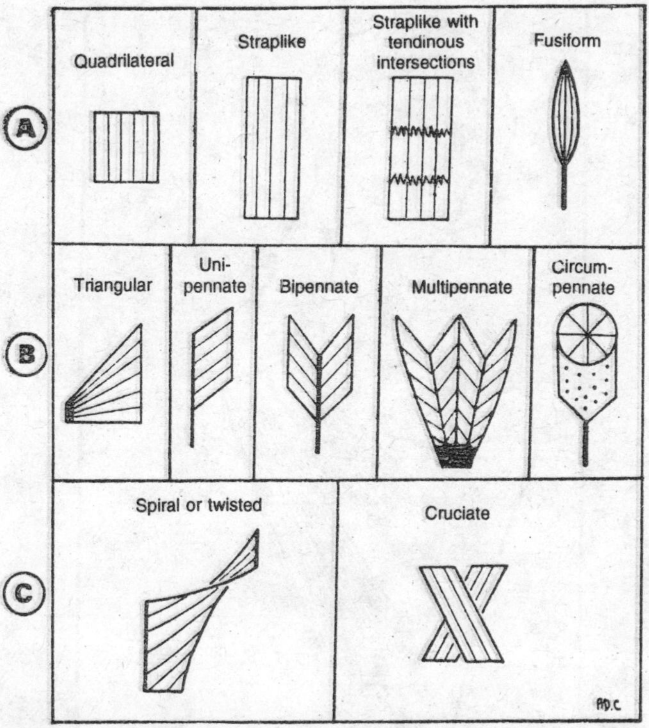

Fig. 4.5. Fascicular architecture of the skeletal muscle. (A) parallel fasciculi; (B) oblique fasciculi; and (C) twisted fasciculi.

A. **Parallel Fasciculi.** When the fasciculi are parallel to the line of pull, the muscle may be : (1) *quadrilateral* (thyrohyoid), (2) *straplike* (sternohyoid and sartorius), (3) *straplike with tendinous intersections* (rectus abdominis), or (4) *fusiform* (biceps, digastric, etc.). The range of movement in such muscles is maximum.

B. **Oblique Fasciculi.** When the fasciculi are oblique to the line of pull, the muscle may be triangular, or pennate (feather-like) in the construction. This arrangement makes the muscle more powerful, although the range of movement is reduced. Oblique arrangements are of the following types :

1. *Triangular*, e.g., temporalis, adductor longus (Fig. 4.6).
2. *Unipennate*, e.g., flexor pollicis longus, extensor digitorum longus, peroneus tertius (Fig. 4.7A).
3. *Bipennate*, e.g., rectus femoris, dorsal interossei, peroneus longus, flexor hallucis longus (Fig. 4.7B).
4. *Multipennate*, e.g., deltoid, subscapularis (Fig. 4.7C).
5. *Circumpennate*, e.g., tibialis anterior.

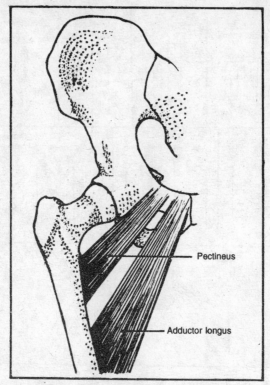

Fig. 4.6. Triangular adductor longus.

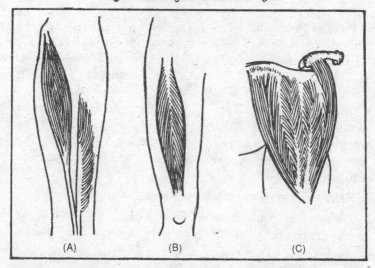

Fig. 4.7. Types of muscle structure. A. Fusiform (flexor carpi radialis) and unipennate (flexor pollicis longus). B. Bipennate (rectus femoris). C. Multipennate (deltoid).

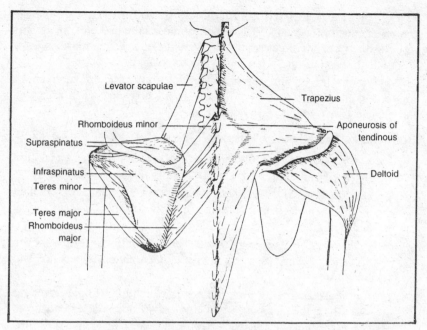

Fig. 4.8. Shoulder region (Posterior view).

Levator scapulae

Rhomboideus minor

Supraspinatus

Infraspinatus

Teres minor

Teres major

Rhomboideus major

Trapezius

Aponeurosis of tendinous

Deltoid

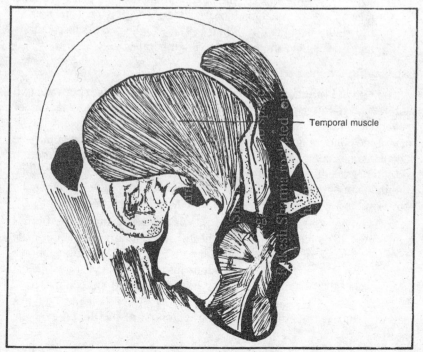

Temporal muscle

Fig. 4.9. Temporalis muscle.

C. **Spiral or Twisted Fasciculi.** Twisted fibres are found in trapezius, pectoralis major, latissimus dorsi, supinator, etc. In certain muscles the fasciculi are crossed. These are called *cruciate* muscles, e.g., sternocleidomastoid, masseter, and adductor magnus.

Many muscles exhibit regional variations in structure, and are a mixture of the foregoing types. Thus, it is possible that when a part of the muscle is active the rest is quiescent.

Bone Marks Produced by Muscles

1. *Fleshly origins* generally leave no mark, although the area is often flattened and depressed, e.g., pectoralis major on clavicle.

2. *Pure tendons and ligaments* always leave a smooth mark which is either elevated or depressed, e.g., insertion of spinati, psoas and obturators, and cruciate ligaments.

3. *Admixture of flesh and tendon* or *a lengthy insertion of an aponeurosis*, makes a rough mark, e.g., gluteal tuberosity and linea aspera.

4. *Flat muscles arising from flat bones* which have to play over the surface of the flat bones : (a) the origin does not extend up to the edge but is set back from the edge in a curved line; (b) between the edge of the bone and curved line there is a bare area where contracting muscle slides; and (c) the bare area is invariably occupied by a bursa. The examples are subscapularis and iliacus, and the exception is temporalis.

Lubricating Mechanisms

1. **Synovial bursae.** Bursa is a device to reduce friction between two mobile but tightly apposed surfaces, permitting complete freedom of movement within limited range. Structurally, it is closed sac of synovial membrane containing a capillary film of synovial fluid. A bursa may be subcutaneous, subtendinous, submuscular, subfascial (subaponeurotic), and interligamentous. Bursa communicating with a joint cavity is called communicating bursa. New (adventitious) bursae may develop where the skin is subjected to repetitive displacements under pressure.

2. **Synovial sheaths.** The tendons, while passing under the fibrous bands, are surrounded by synovial sheaths. Structurally, these are made up of two concentric layers (parietal and visceral) of synovial membrane produced by invagination of the tendons into the sheath. The two layers are separated by a capillary film of synovial fluid and are continuous at their extremities. The mesotendon may either disappear completely, or may be reduced to cords, like vincula tendinum of the digital synovial sheaths.

3. **Cartilage modification of periosteum** (Kate, 1971). The periosteum at the site of tendinous contact becomes modified into hyaline cartilage, or fibrocartilage, or an admixture of both, thus providing a slippery surface for free movement of the tendon.

Nomenclature of Muscles (Figs. 4.3, 4.6-4.9)

The muscles have been named in a number of ways.

1. According to their shape, e.g., trapezius, rhomboideus, serratus anterior, latissimus dorsi, etc.
2. According to the number of heads of origin, e.g., biceps, triceps, quadriceps, digastric, etc.
3. According to their gross structure, e.g., semitendinosus, semimembranosus, etc.
4. According to their location, e.g., temporalis, supraspinatus, intercostales, etc.
5. According to their attachments, e.g., stylohyoid, cricothyroid, etc.
6. According to their function, e.g., adductor longus, flexor carpi ulnaris, abductor pollicis longus, etc.
7. According to direction of their fibres, e.g., rectus abdominis, obliquus abdominis, transversus, etc.

Blood Supply of Skeletal Muscle

Blood supply is derived from muscular branches from the neighbouring arteries. The arteries, veins and motor nerve pierce the muscle at a fairly constant point called neurovascular hilum. Subsidiary arteries may enter the muscle near the ends. The arteries divide repeatedly to form arterioles in the perimysium, and capillaries in the endomysium for nutritive circulation. Arteriovenous anastomoses are abundant in the epimysium and perimysium for non-nutritive circulation during muscular contraction. Presence of arteriovenous anastomoses in certain experimental animals was demonstrated by Jaya (1957), but denied by Sadasivan and Hanmant Rao (1964).

Lymphatics accompany the vessels and drain into the neighbouring nodes.

Nerve Supply of Skeletal Muscle

The nerve supplying a muscle is called motor nerve. In fact it is a mixed nerve, and consists of the following types of fibres.

1. **Motor fibres** (60%) comprise : (a) large myelinated alpha efferents which supply extrafusal muscle fibres; (b) smaller myelinated gamma efferents which supply intrafusal fibres of the muscle spindles; and (c) the fine non-myelinated autonomic efferents which supply smooth muscle fibres of the blood vessels.

2. **Sensory fibres** (40%) comprise : (a) myelinated fibres distributed to muscle spindles, tendons and local fascia; and (b) non-myelinated fibres carrying pain sensations of uncertain origin.

Motor point is the site where the motor nerve enters the muscle. It may be one or more than one. Electrical stimulation at the motor point is more effective.

Motor unit (myone) is defined as a single alpha motor neuron together with the muscle fibres supplied by it. The size of motor unit depends upon the precision of muscle control. Small motor units (5-10 muscle fibres) are found in muscles of fine movements (extra-ocular muscles). Large motor units (100-2000 muscle fibres) are found in muscles of gross movements (proximal limb muscles).

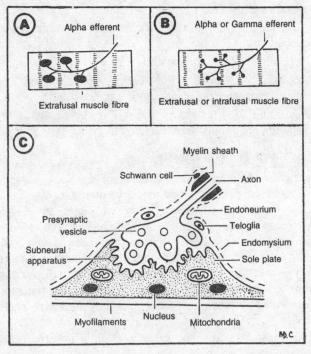

Fig. 4.10. Neuromuscular junctions. (A) en plaque terminals, or motor end plates; (B) en grappe terminals; (C) ultrastructure of a motor end plate.

Neuromuscular junctions are cholinergic in nature. On approaching the muscle the axons of motor nerve lose their myelin sheath and break up into a number of branches to supply the individual muscle fibres. The specialized motor nerve endings, rich in acetylcholine, are of two types : (a) **'en plaque' terminals** (Fig. 4.10A) are plate-like (plaque = plate), and are known as *motor end plates*. These are found in most of the skeletal muscles of the body. (b) **'en grappe' terminals** (Fig. 4.10B) resemble a bunch of grapes (grappe = grape), and are found in extraocular muscles and tail endings of the muscle spindle. At the neuromuscular junction, the muscle fibre also is specialized into a *sole plate*, which is a localized collection of granular sarcoplasm containing many nuclei and mitochondria, and presenting synaptic gutters for the end plate (Fig. 4.10C). The motor end plate and sole plate are separated by an ultra-microscopic gap. The sacrolemmal folds (subneural clefts) in the synaptic gutter are rich in acetylcholinesterase which destroys the liberated acetylcholine after each neuromuscular transmission of impulse.

Muscle spindles (neuromuscular spindles) are spindle-shaped sensory end organs of the skeletal muscle. Each spindle contains 6-14 intrafusal muscle fibres which are of two types, the larger *nuclear bag fibres*, and the smaller *nuclear chain fibres* (Fig. 4.11). The spindle is innervated by both the sensory and motor nerves. The sensory endings are of two types, the primary sensory endings (*annulospiral endings*) around the central nuclear region of the intrafusal fibres, and the secondary sensory endings (*flower spray endings*) beyond the nuclear region on either side of these fibres. The motor nerve supply of the spindle is derived from gamma motor neurons of the spinal cord, which form both the 'en plaque' and 'en grappe' terminals. Muscles spindles act as stretch receptors. They record and help regulate the degree and rate of contraction of the extrafusal fibres by influencing the alpha neurons. Recent evidence shows that the spindle activity is represented in the sensory cortex, which plays a part in conscious appreciation of the position and movements of the joints.

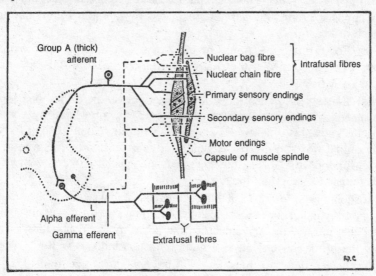

Fig. 4.11. Structure and nerve supply of the muscle spindle.

Actions of Muscles

1. Broadly, when a muscle contracts it shortens by 1/3 (30%) of its belly-length, and brings about a movement. The range of movement depends on the length of fleshy fibres, and the power or force of movement on the number of fibres.

However, the actual behaviour of muscle contraction is more complex. During contraction the length of the muscle may decrease (isotonic contraction), may remain unchanged (isometric contraction), or may increase, according to the functional demands of the body. In each circumstance the tension generated at the ends may either increase, persist, or decrease, depending upon the number and state of its active motor units and the external conditions like loading.

2. Each movement at a joint is brought about by a coordinated activity of different groups of muscles. These muscle groups are classified and named according to their function.

(a) **Prime movers (agonists)** bring about the desired movement. When a prime mover helps opposite action by active controlled lengthening against gravity, it is known as *action of paradox*. For example, putting a glass back on the table is assisted by gravity but controlled by a gradual active lengthening of biceps (paradoxical or eccentric action).

(b) **Antagonists (opponents)** oppose the prime movers. They help the prime movers by active controlled relaxation, so that the desired movement is smooth and precise. Thus, the antagonists cooperate rather than oppose the prime movers. This is due to reciprocal innervation of this opposite groups of muscles, regulated by the spinal cord through stretch reflex.

(c) **Fixators** are the groups of muscles which stabilize the proximal joints of a limb, so that the desired movement at the distal joint may occur on a fixed base.

(d) **Synergists.** When the prime movers cross more than one joint, the undesired actions at the proximal joints are prevented by certain muscles known as synergists. For example, during making a tight fist by long digital flexors the wrist is kept fixed in extension by the synergists (extensors of wrist). Thus, the synergists are special fixators and partial antagonists to the prime movers.

It should be appreciated that the same muscle may act as prime mover, antagonist, fixator, or synergist, under different circumstances. It is also clear that most of the movements of the body involve contraction of not only the prime movers but of a number of assistants as well.

3. The actions of muscles can be tested (a) anatomically, by dissection, (b) electromyographically (Basmajian, 1967; MacConail and Basmajian, 1977), and (c) clinically.

Some Definitions

Isotonic or concentric contraction occurs if the length of muscles is reduced by 1/3 or more.

During isometric contraction the tension is same as load and length of the muscles does not change, e.g., holding the arm outstretched.

During excentric contraction, tension is less than the load, i.e., muscle fibres are lengthening to bring about a particular movement, e.g., lowering the arm to the side.

Active insufficiency : A particular tendon crossing number of joints cannot work with efficiency at all the joints of the same time, e.g., flexor digitorum profundus muscles on the wrist, metacarpo-phalangeal and interphalangeal joints.

Passive insufficiency : The extensors cannot extend all the joints at the same time, e.g., extensor digitorum on the wrist and joints of metacarpals and phalanges.

MECHANICS OF A MUSCLES

When a muscle contracts the force of contraction is said to have three components, e.g.,

(i) Swing which is transaxial. This component is maximum during the contraction of brachialis muscle while flexing the elbow joint.

(ii) Shunt which is transarticular. Shunt component is maximum when the origin of the muscle is close to a joint while insertion is at a distance, e.g., brachioradialis muscle.

(iii) Spin which is rotary along its axis. Spin component is predominant in the pronator quadratus muscle, wrapped on the anterior surfaces of lower ends of radius and ulna bones.

Applied Anatomy

1. **Paralysis.** Loss of motor power (power of movement) is called paralysis. This is due to inability of the muscles to contract caused either by damage to the motor neural pathways (upper or lower motor neuron), or by the inherent disease of muscles (myopathy). Damage to the upper motor neuron causes spastic paralysis with exaggerated tendon jerks. Damage to the lower motor neuron causes *flaccid paralysis* with loss of tendon jerks.

2. **Muscular spasm.** These are quite painful. Localized muscle spasm is commonly caused by a 'muscle pull'. In order to relieve its pain the muscle should be relaxed by appropriate treatment. Generalized muscle spasms occur in tetanus and epilepsy.

3. **Disused atrophy and hypertrophy.** The muscles which are not used for long times become thin and weak. This is called *disused atrophy*. Conversely, adequate or excessive use of particular muscles causes their better development, or even *hypertrophy*. Muscular 'wasting' (reduction in size) is a feature of lower motor neuron paralysis and generalized debility.

4. **Regeneration of skeletal muscle.** Skeletal muscle is capable of limited regeneration. If large regions are damaged, regeneration does not occur and the missing muscle is replaced by connective tissue.

REFERENCES AND SUGGESTIONS
FOR ADDITIONAL READING

Basmajian, J.V. (1967). *Muscles Alive*, 2nd ed. Williams and Wilkins, Baltimore.

Burke, R.E., Levine, D. and Tsiaris, P. (1973). Physiological types and histochemical profiles in motor units of the cat gastrocnemius. *J. Physiol., Lond.*, 234 : 723-748.

Dubowitz, V. (1969). Histochemical aspects of muscle disease. In : *Disorders of Voluntary Muscle* (Walton, J.N. ed.), Churchill, London.

Gauthier, G.F. and Schaeffer, S.F. (1974). Ultrastructural and cytochemical manifestations of protein synthesis in the peripheral sarcoplasm of denervated and newborn skeletal muscle fibres. *J. Cell Sci.*, 143 : 113-137.

Jaya, Y. (1957). A brief exposition of AVA, histologically and radiologically. *Proc. Acad. Med. Sc., Hyderabad*, 1 : 15-21.

Jaya, Y. (1962). Quantitative anatomy of the capillaries in the rat muscles. *J. Anat. Soc. India*, 11 : 32-34.

Kate, B.R. (1971). The cartilage modification of the periosteum. *J. Anat. Soc. India*, 20 : 28-32.

MacConail, M.A. and Basmajian, J.V. (1977). *Muscles and Movements*. Krieger Publishing Company, New York.

Sadasivan, G. and Hanmant Rao, G. (1964). Arteriovenous anastomosis in skeletal muscle. *J. Anat. Soc. India*, 13 : 90-95.

5

Cardiovascular System

Cardiovascular system is the transport system of the body, through which the nutrients are conveyed to places where these are utilized, and the metabolites (waste products) are conveyed to appropriate places from where these are excreted. The conveying medium is a liquid tissue, the blood, which flows in tubular channels called blood vessels. The circulation is maintained by the central pumping organ called the heart.

Components

It is a closed system of tubes made up of the following parts based on their structural and topographical characteristics (Fig. 5.1).

1. **Heart.** It is a four-chambered muscular organ which pumps blood to various parts of the body. Each half of the heart has a receiving chamber called atrium, and a pumping chamber called ventricle.

2. **Arteries.** These are distributing channels which carry blood away from the heart. They branch like trees on their way to different parts of the body. The large arteries are rich in elastic tissue, but as branching progresses there is an ever-increasing amount of smooth muscle in their walls. The minute branches which are just visible to naked eye are called *arterioles*.

3. **Veins.** These are draining channels which carry blood from different parts of the body back to the heart. Like rivers, the veins are formed by tributaries. The small veins (venules) join together to form larger veins, which in turn unite to form great veins called venae cavae.

Capillaries. These are networks of microscopic vessels which connect arterioles with the venules. They come in intimate contact with the tissues for a free exchange of nutrients and metabolites across their walls between the blood and the tissue fluid. The metabolites are partly drained by the capillaries and partly by lymphatics. Capillaries are replaced by sinusoids in certain organs, like liver and spleen.

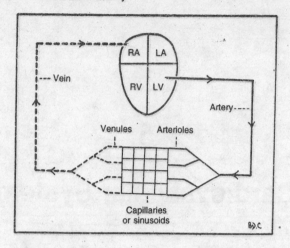

Fig. 5.1. Components of the cardiovascular system.
Arrows indicate the direction of the blood flow.
RA = right atrium;
LA = left atrium;
RV = right ventricle;
LV = left ventricle.

Functionally, the blood vessels can be classified into five groups : (a) *distributing vessels*, including arteries; (b) *resistance vessels*, including arterioles and precapillary sphincters; (c) *exchange vessels*, including capillaries, sinusoids, and postcapillary venules; (d) *reservoir (capacitance) vessels*, including larger venules and veins; and (e) *shunts*, including various types of anastomoses.

Types of Circulation of Blood (Fig. 5.2 & 5.3)

A. **Systemic (greater) circulation.** The blood flows from the left ventricle, through various parts of the body, to the right atrium, i.e., from the left to the right side of the heart.

B. **Pulmonary (lesser) circulation.** The blood flows from the right ventricle, through the lungs, to the left atrium, i.e., from the right to the left side of the heart.

C. **Portal circulation.** It is a part of systemic circulation, which has the following characteristics : (a) The blood passes through two sets of capillaries before draining into a systemic vein. (b) The vein draining the first capillary network is known as portal vein which branches like an artery to form the second set of capillaries or sinusoids. Examples : hepatic, hypophyseal and renal portal circulations.

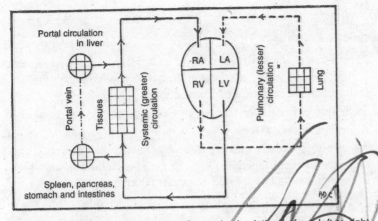

Fig. 5.2. Types of blood circulation. Systemic circulation is from left to right (from left ventricle to right atrium). Pulmonary circulation is from right to left (from right ventricle to left atrium). When blood passes through a second set of capillaries it is called portal circulation, RA = right atrium; LA = left atrium; RV = right ventricle; LV = left ventricle.

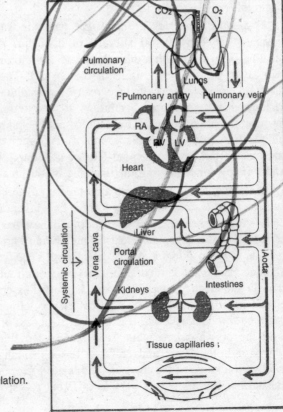

Fig. 5.3. Types of circulation.

ARTERIES

Characteristic Features

1. Arteries are *thick-walled*, being uniformly thicker than the accompanying veins, except for the arteries within the cranium and vertebral canal where they are thin.
2. Their *lumen is smaller* than that of the accompanying veins.
3. Arteries have no valves.
4. An artery is usually accompanied by vein(s) and nerve(s), and the three of them together form the neurovascular bundle which is surrounded and supported by a fibroareolar sheath.

Types of Arteries and Structure

1. *Large arteries of elastic type*, e.g., aorta and its main branches (brachiocephalic, common carotid, subclavian and common iliac) and the pulmonary arteries.

2. *Medium and small arteries of muscular type*, e.g., temporal, occipital, radial, popliteal, etc.

3. *Smallest arteries of muscular type* are called arterioles. They measure between 50-100 microns in diameter. Arterioles divide into terminal arterioles with a diameter of 15-20 microns, and having one or two layers of smooth muscle in their walls. The side branches from *terminal arterioles* are called *metarterioles* which measure 10-15 microns at their origin and about 5 microns at their termination. The terminal narrow end is surrounded by a precapillary sphincter which regulates blood flow into the capillary bed. It is important to know that the muscular arterioles are responsible for generating peripheral resistance, and thereby for regulating the diastolic blood pressure.

Microscopically, all arteries are made up of three coats. (a) The inner coat is called *tunica intima*. It is formed by a layer of flattened endothelial cells, supported externally by subendothelial areolar tissue (longitudinally arranged) and a fenestrated elastic membrane known as internal elastic lamina. (b) The middle coat is called *tunica media*. It is the thickest of all coats, and is made up of alternate layers of circularly arranged smooth muscle and elastic tissue. This layer is limited externally by a fenestrated elastic membrane known as external elastic lamina. (c) The outer coat is called *tunica adventitia*. It is thin but strongest of all coats and merges with the perivascular sheath. It is made up of longitudinally arranged fibres of both elastic and collagen tissue, making it fibroelastic. The relative thickness of the coats and the relative proportion of the muscular, elastic and fibrous tissues vary in different types of arteries.

Blood Supply of Arteries

The large arteries (of more than 1 mm diameter) are supplied with blood vessels. The nutrient vessels, called *vasa vasorum*, form a dense capillary network in the tunica adventitia, and supply the adventitia and the outer part of tunica media. The rest of the vessel wall (intima + inner part of media) is nourished directly by diffusion from the luminal blood. Fenestrations in the elastic laminae facilitate this diffusion.

Minute veins accompanying the arteries drain the blood from the outer part of arterial wall.

Lymphatics are also present in the adventitia.

Nerve Supply of Arteries

The nerves supplying an artery are called *nervi vascularis*. The nerves are mostly non-myelinated sympathetic fibres which are vasoconstrictor in function. A few fibres are myelinated, and are believed to be sensory to the outer and inner coats of the arteries.

Vasodilator innervation is restricted to the following sites. (a) The skeletal muscle vessels are dilated by *cholinergic sympathetic nerves*. (b) The exocrine gland vessels are dilated by the polypeptide *bradykinin* formed from alpha-2 globulins (in the plasma) by the action of the enzyme kallikrein which is released in the glands on parasympathetic stimulation. (c) The cutaneous vessels are dilated locally to produce the flare (redness) after an injury. The vasodilatation is produced by the afferent impulses in the cutaneous nerves which pass antidromically in their collaterals to the blood vessels (*axon reflex*).

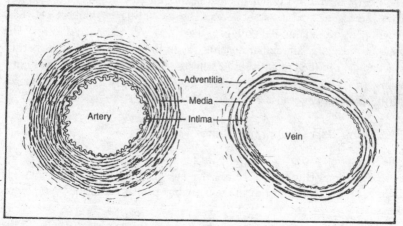

Fig. 5.4. Artery and vein — transverse section.

VEINS

Characteristic Features

1. Veins are *thin-walled*, being thinner than the arteries.
2. Their *lumen is larger* than that of the accompanying arteries.
3. Veins have valves which maintain the unidirectional flow of blood, even against gravity. Since the venous pressure is low (7 mm Hg), the valves are of utmost value in the venous return. However, the valves are absent : (a) in the veins of less than 2 mm in diameter; (b) in the venae cavae; and (c) in the hepatic, renal, uterine, ovarian (not testicular), cerebral, spinal, pulmonary, and umbilical veins.
4. The muscular and elastic tissue content of the venous walls is much less than that of the arteries. This is directly related to the low venous pressure.
5. Large veins have *dead space* around them for their dilatation during increased venous return. The dead space commonly contains the regional lymph nodes.

Structure of Veins

Veins are made up of usual three coats which are found in the arteries. But the coats are ill-defined, and the muscle and elastic tissue content is poor.

A proper internal elastic lamina in the intima is absent. In the weak and poorly developed tunica media, the amount of collagen fibres is more than the elastic and muscle fibres. The adventitia is thickest and best developed; it contains the collagen, elastic as well as muscle fibres. The smooth muscle is altogether absent : (a) in the veins of maternal part of placenta; (b) in the cranial venous sinuses and pial veins; (c) in the retinal veins; (d) in the veins of cancellous bone; and (e) in the venous spaces of the corpora cavernosa and corpus spongiosum.

Blood and Nerve Supply of Veins

The larger veins, like the arteries, are supplied with nutrient vessels called *vasa vasorum*. But in the veins, the vessels may penetrate up to the intima, probably because of the low venous pressure and the low oxygen tension.

Nerves also are distributed to the veins in the same manner as to the arteries, but are fewer in number.

Factors Helping in Venous Return

1. Overflow from the capillaries, pushed from behind by the arteries (*vis-a-tergo*).
2. *Negative intrathoracic pressure* sucks the blood into the heart from all over the body.
3. *Gravity* helps venous return in the upper part of the body.
4. *Arterial pulsations* press on the venae comitantes intermittently and drive the venous blood towards the heart.
5. Venous *valves* prevent any regurgitation (back flow) of the luminal blood.
6. Muscular contractions press on the veins and form a very effective mechanism of venous return. This becomes still more effective within the tight sleeve of the deep fascia, as is seen in the lower limbs. The calf muscles (soleus) for this reason are known as the peripheral heart. Thus the *muscle pumps* are important factors in the venous return (Fig. 5.5).

CAPILLARIES

Capillaries (capillus = hair) are networks of microscopic endothelial tubes interposed between the metarterioles and venules (Fig. 5.1). The true capillaries (without any smooth muscle cell) begin after a transition zone of 50-100 microns beyond the precapillary sphincters. The capillaries are replaced by cavernous (dilated) spaces in the sex organs, splenic pulp and placenta.

Size

The average diameter of a capillary is 6-8 microns, just sufficient to permit the red blood cells to pass through in 'single file'. But the size varies from organ to organ. It is smallest in the brain and intestines, and is largest (20 microns) in the skin and bone marrow.

Types and Structure

The capillaries are classified as continuous and fenestrated according to the type of junctions between the endothelial cells.

1. *Continuous capillaries* are found in the skin, connective tissue, skeletal and smooth muscles, lung and brain. They allow passage across their walls of small molecules (up to 10 mm size).
2. *Fenestrated capillaries* are found in the renal glomeruli, intestinal mucosa, endocrine glands and pancreas. They allow passage across their walls of larger molecules (up to 20-100 nm size).

The capillary wall is composed of :

(a) a single layer of endothelial cells;

(b) a basal lamina of glycoprotein which surrounds the endothelial cells and splits at places to enclose pericapillary cells called pericytes; and

(c) a pericapillary layer of connective tissue cells and fibres.

The capillary bed and postcapillary venules form an enormous area for the exchange of nutrients, gases, metabolites and water, between the blood and interstitial fluid. Capillaries also allow migration of leucocytes out of the vessels.

SINUSOIDS

Sinusoids replace capillaries in certain organs, like liver, spleen, bone marrow, suprarenal glands, parathyroid glands, carotid body, etc.

Characteristics

Sinusoids are large, irregular, vascular spaces which are closely surrounded by the parenchyma of the organ. They differ from capillaries in the following respects;

1. Their lumen is *wider* (upto 30 microns) and *irregular.*

2. Their walls are *thinner* and may be incomplete. They are lined by endothelium in which the phagocytic cells (*macrophages*) are often distributed. The adventitial support is absent, and the basal lamina is replaced by a thin layer of reticular fibres.

3. They may connect arteriole with venule (spleen, bone marrow), or venule with venule (liver).

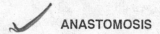 ## ANASTOMOSIS

Definition

A precapillary or postcapillary communication between the neighbouring vessels is called anastomosis. Circulation through the anastomosis is called *collateral circulation.*

Types

A. **Arterial anastomosis** is the communication between the arteries or branches of arteries. It may be actual or potential. (1) In *actual arterial anastomosis* the arteries meet end to end. For example, palmar arches, plantar arch, circle of Willis, intestinal arcades around the stomach, labial branches of facial arteries, and the uterine and ovarian arteries. (2) In *potential arterial anastomosis* the communication takes place between the terminal arterioles. Such communications can dilate only gradually for collateral circulation. Therefore on sudden occlusion of a main artery, the anastomosis may fail to compensate the loss. The examples are seen in the coronary arteries, around the limb joints; the cortical branches of cerebral arteries, etc. (Fig. 5.6-5.8).

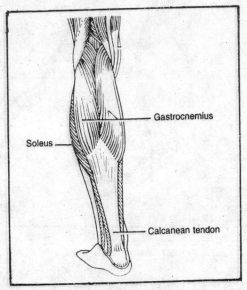

Fig. 5.5. Calf muscles.

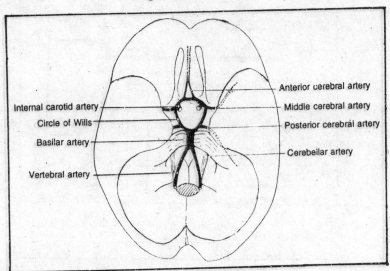

Fig. 5.6. Arteries of the base of the brain.

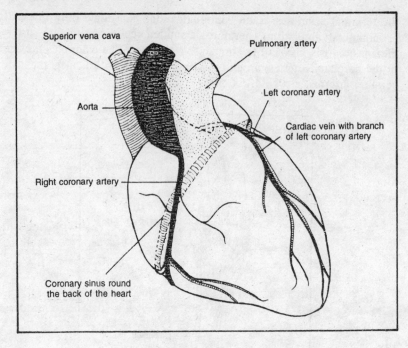

Fig. 5.7. Blood vessels of the heart.

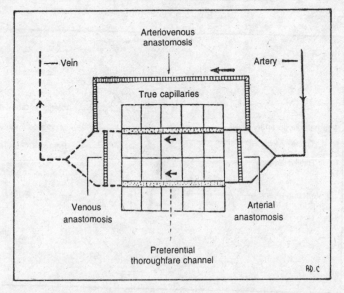

Fig. 5.8. Diagram showing different types of anastomoses. Arrows indicate the direction of the blood flow.

B. **Venous anastomosis** is the communication between the veins or tributaries of veins. For example, the dorsal venous arches of the hand and foot.

C. **Arteriovenous anastomosis (shunt)** is the communication between an artery and a vein. It serves the function of phasic activity of the organ. When the organ is active these shunts are closed and the blood circulates through the capillaries. However, when the organ is at rest, the blood bypasses the capillary bed and is shunted back through the arteriovenous anastomosis. The shunt vessel may be straight or coiled, possesses a thick muscular coat, and is under the influence of sympathetic system. Shunts of *simple* structure are found in the skin of nose, lips and external ear; in the mucous membrane of nose and alimentary canal; the coccygeal body; the erectile tissue of sexual organs; the tongue; the thyroid gland and sympathetic ganglia. *Specialized* arteriovenous anastomoses are found in the skin of digital pads and nail beds. They form a number of small units called *glomera.*

Preferential 'thoroughfare channels' are also a kind of shunts. They course through the capillary networks. Many true capillaries arise as their side branches. One thoroughfare channel with its associated capillaries forms a *microcirculatory unit.* The size of the unit is variable from 1-2 to 20-30 true capillaries. The number of active units varies from time to time.

END-ARTERIES

Definition

Arteries which do not anastomose with their neighbours are called end-arteries. Examples : (1) central artery of retina is the best example of an absolute end-artery; (2) central branches of cerebral arteries and vasa recta of mesenteric arteries; (3) arteries of spleen, kidney, lungs and metaphyses of long bones.

Importance

Occlusion of an end-artery causes serious nutritional disturbances resulting in death of the tissue supplied by it. For example, occlusion of central artery of retina results in permanent blindness.

APPLIED ANATOMY OF CVS

1. The **'blood pressure'** is the arterial pressure exerted by the blood on the arterial walls. The maximum pressure during ventricular systole is called *systolic pressure*; the minimum pressure during ventricular diastole is called *diastolic pressure*. The systolic pressure is generated by the force of contraction of the heart; the diastolic pressure is chiefly

due to arteriolar tone (peripheral resistance). The heart has to pump the blood against the diastolic pressure which is a direct load on the heart. Normally, the blood pressure is roughly 120/80 mm Hg, the systolic pressure ranging from 110-140, and the diastolic pressure from 70-90. The difference between systolic and diastolic pressure is called '*pulse pressure*'.

2. **Haemorrhage** (bleeding) is the obvious result of rupture of the blood vessels. Venous haemorrhage causes oozing of blood; arterial haemorrhage causes spurting of blood.

3. **Vascular catastrophies** are of three types : (a) thrombosis; (b) embolism; and (c) haemorrhage. All of them result in a loss of blood supply to the area of distribution of the vessel involved, unless it is compensated by collateral circulation.

4. **Arteriosclerosis.** In old age the arteries become stiff. This phenomenon it called arteriosclerosis. This causes a variable reduction in the blood supply to the tissues and a rise in systolic pressure.

5. **Arteritis and Phlebitis.** Inflammation of an artery is known as arteritis, and inflammation of a vein as phlebitis.

6. *Angeion* is a Greek word, meaning a vessel (blood vessel or lymph vessel). Its word derivatives are angiology, angiography, haemangioma, and thromboangitis obliterans.

REFERENCES AND SUGGESTIONS
FOR ADDITIONAL READING

Bennett, H.S., Luft, J.S. and Hampton, J.C. (1957). Morphological classification of vertebrate blood capillaries. *Am. J. Physiol.*, 196 : 381-390.

Clark, E.R. (1938). Arteriovenous anastomosis. *Physiol. Rev.*, 18 : 229-247.

Grant, R.T. and Payling Wright, H. (1970). Anatomical basis for non-nutritive circulation is skeletal muscle exemplified by blood vessels of rat biceps femoris tendon. *J. Anat.*, 106 : 125-134.

Rhodin, J.A.G. (1962). The diaphragm of capillary endothelial fenestrations. *J. Ultrastruct. Res.*, 6 : 171-185.

Rhodin, J.A.G. (1967). Ultrastructure of mammalian arterioles and precapillary sphincters. *J. Ultrastruct. Res.*, 18 : 181-223.

Rhodin, J.A.G. (1968). Ultrastructure of mammalian venous capillaries, venules and small collecting veins. *J. Ultrastruct. Res.*, 25 : 452-500.

Simionescu, N., Simionescu, M. and Palade, G.E. (1975). Permeability of muscle capillaries to small hemepeptides. Evidence for the existence of patent transendothelial channels. *J. Cell Biol.*, 64 : 586-607.

Zweifach, B.W. (1959). The microcirculation of the blood. *Scient. Am.*, 200 : 54-60.

6

Lymphatic System

Lymphatic system is essentially a drainage system which is accessory to the venous system (Fig. 6.1). Most of the tissue fluid formed at the arterial end of capillaries is absorbed back into the blood by the venous ends of the capillaries and the postcapillary venules. The rest of the tissue fluid (10-20%) is absorbed by the lymphatics which begin blindly in the tissue spaces. It is important to know that the larger particles (proteins and particulate matter) can be removed from the tissue fluid only by the lymphatics. Therefore, the lymphatic system may be regarded as 'drainage system of coarse type' and the venous system as 'drainage system of fine type'. Certain parts of the lymphatic system (lymphoreticular organs), however, are chiefly involved in phagocytosis, raising immune responses, and contributing to cell populations of the blood and lymph.

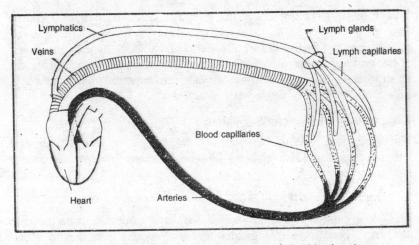

Fig. 6.1. The relationship of the lymph system to the blood system.

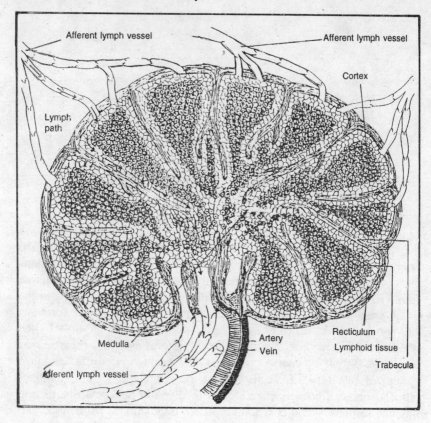

Fig. 6.2. Structure of a lymph node.

The tissue fluid flowing in the lymphatic is called lymph. It passes through filters (lymph nodes) (Fig. 6.2) placed in the course of lymphatics, and finally drains into the venous blood. Lymph from most of the tissues is clear and colourless, but the lymph from small intestine is milk-white due to absorption of fat. The intestinal milky lymph is called *chyle*, and the lymph vessels lacteals.

Components of Lymphatic System

The lymphatic system comprises : (1) lymph vessels; (2) central lymphoid tissues; (3) peripheral lymphoid organs; and (4) circulating lymphocytes.

1. Lymph Vessels (Fig. 6.3-6.5)

The lymph capillaries begin blindly in the tissue spaces and form intricate networks. Their calibre is greater and less regular than that of blood capillaries, and their endothelial wall is permeable to substances of much greater molecular size (Allen, 1967). Lymph capillaries are absent from the avascular structures, brain, spinal cord, splenic pulp, and bone marrow.

From the lymph capillaries there are several alternative routes of lymphatics to the regional lymph nodes. This accounts for variable descriptions of the lymphatic drainage in different textbooks. The superficial lymphatics accompany veins, while the deep lymphatics accompany arteries or veins.

The lymph passes through filters or barriers of the regional lymph nodes which trap the particulate matter. The filtered lymph passes through larger lymphatics and is eventually collected into two large trunks, the thoracic duct and right lymphatic duct, which pour their lymph into the brachiocephalic veins.

The lymphatics anastomose freely with their neighbours of the same side as well as of the opposite side. Larger lymphatics are supplied with their vasa vasorum and are accompanied by a plexus of fine blood vessels which form red streaks seen in lymphangitis. Lymph vessels have great power of regeneration after their damage.

2. Central Lymphoid Tissues

Central Lymphoid tissues comprise bone marrow and thymus. All 'pluripotent' lymphoid stem cells are initially produced by bone marrow,

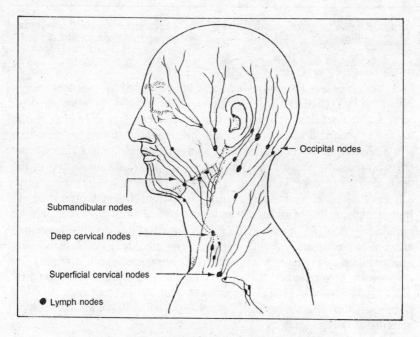

Fig. 6.3. Some lymph nodes of the face and neck.

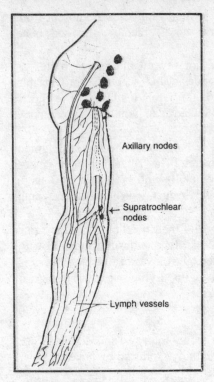

Fig. 6.4. Some lymph nodes of the upper limb.

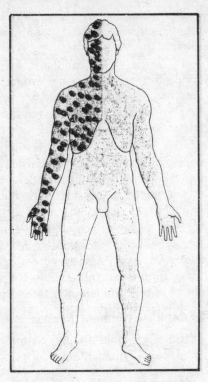

Fig. 6.5. Lymph drainage. Shaded area drained by the thoracic duct. Dotted area drained by the right lymphatic duct.

except during early fetal life when these are produced by liver and spleen. The stem cells undergo differentiation in the central lymphoid tissues, so that the lymphocytes become competent defensive elements of the immune system. Bone marrow helps differentiation of the (committed) B-lymphocytes which are capable of synthesizing antibodies after getting transformed into plasma cells; in birds, B-cells are differentiated in the wall of the bursa of Fabricius, a hindgut diverticulum. *Thymus* helps differentiation of immunologically competent but uncommitted T-lymphocytes (10% of thymic population) which are long-lived, join the circulating pool of lymphocytes, and populate the thymus-dependent areas of lymph nodes and other peripheral lymphoid organs. T-cells being uncommitted can react to a wide range of foreign antigenic stimuli. They respond by cytotoxic cell killing (killing virus-infected cells, neoplastic cells, fungi, tissue grafts, etc.), by 'arming' macrophages, and by triggering the large mononuclear cells (killer cells) and the 'helper' activity of B-lymphocytes.

3. Peripheral Lymphoid Organs

Peripheral lymphoid organs comprise lymph nodes, spleen, and epithelio-lymphoid tissues (lymphoid nodules developed in the alimentary and respiratory tracts). Any part of this may become overactive on appropriate stimulation.

The progenies of B- and T-lymphocytes reach these organs where the cells may proliferate and mature into competent cells. The mature lymphocytes join the circulating pool of lymphocytes.

4. Circulating Pool of Lymphocytes

The pool contains mature progenies of B- and T-lymphocytes which may be called upon during antigenic emergencies (Roitt, 1977).

Lymphatic Follicle (Nodule)

Collections of lymphocytes occur at many places in the body. Everywhere there is a basic pattern, the lymphatic follicle. The follicle is a spherical collection of lymphocytes with a pale centre known as germinal centre, where the lymphocytes are more loosely packed. The central cells are larger in size, stain less deeply, and divide more rapidly, than the peripheral cells.

LYMPH NODES

Lymph nodes are small nodules of lymphoid tissue found in the course of smaller lymphatics. The lymph passes through one or more lymph nodes before reaching the larger lymph trunks. The nodes are oval or reniform in shape, 1-25 mm long, and brown (hepatic), black (pulmonary), or creamy white (intestinal) in colour. Usually they occur in groups (axillary, inguinal, mesenteric, mediastinal, etc.), but at times there may be a solitary lymph node. Superficial nodes are arranged along the veins, and the deep nodes along the arteries.

Each lymph node has a slight depression on one side, called hilum. The artery enters the node, and the vein with efferent lymphatic comes out of it, at the hilum. The afferent lymphatics enter the node at different parts of its periphery.

Structurally, a lymph node is made up of the following parts (Fig. 6.6).

1. **Fibrous and reticular framework.** The lymph node is covered by a capsule made up mainly of collagen fibres and a few elastin fibres. From the deep surface of the capsule a number of trabeculae extend radially into the interior of the node, where they are continuous with the fine reticulum (meshwork of reticulin fibres) which forms the supporting framework for the lymphoid tissue.

2. **Lymphatic channels.** The subcapsular sinus lies beneath the capsule and surrounds the node except at the hilum. The afferent lymphatics of the node open into the subcapsular sinus, which gives rise to numerous *cortical sinuses* running towards the medulla, where they unite with each other to form the larger medullary sinuses, which join together to form the efferent lymphatics (one or two) draining the lymph node. All sinuses are lined by endothelial cells which allow a constant biway passage for lymphocytes, macrophages, and other cells, across the sinus walls.

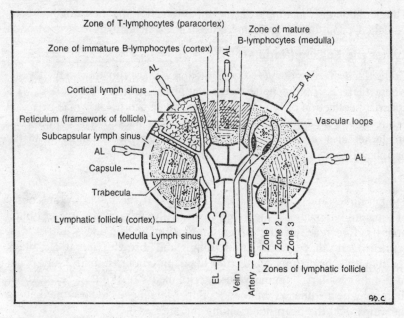

Fig. 6.6. Structure of a lymph node. AL = afferent lymphatics; EL = efferent lymphatic.

3. **Cortex.** It is the outer part of the lymph node situated beneath the subcapsular sinus, being absent at the hilum. It is made up of lymphatic follicles and is traversed by fibrous trabeculae. The cortex is far more densely cellular than the medulla. It is divided into : (a) *zone 1*, containing loosely packed small lymphocytes, macrophages and occasional plasma cells in the periphery of the follicle and extending into the medullary cords; (b) *zone 2*, containing more densely packed small lymphocytes and macrophages, deep to zone 1 and limited to cortical and paracortical (inner cortex) areas; and (c) *zone 3*, including the germinal centre which contains large lymphocytes and macrophages.

The maturing lymphocytes pass from zone 3 to zone 2 to zone 1 and to the lymph sinus (Fig. 6.6).

According to the distribution of B- and T-lymphocytes, the cortex is divided into : (1) an outer part which contains immature B-lymphocytes; and (2) an inner part, between the germinal centre and the medulla, which contains T-lymphocytes. This part is known as *paracortex* or *thymus dependent zone*. The mature B-lymphocytes (plasma cells) are found in the medulla. Whether the germinal centre contains T- or B-cells, or both, is not known.

4. **Medulla.** It is the central part of the lymph node, made up of an interlacement of the trabeculae. The interstitial spaces contain loosely packed lymphocytes (forming irregular branching medullary cords), the plasma cells, and macrophages.

5. **Blood channels.** The artery enters at the hilum and divides into straight branches which run in the trabeculae. In the cortex the arteries further divide to form arcades of arterioles and capillaries with many anastomosing loops. The capillaries give rise to venules and veins, which run back to the hilum. The capillaries are more profuse around the follicles, and the postcapillary venules are more abundant in the para-cortical zones for lymphatic migration.

Haemal Nodes

These are small lymphatic bodies resembling lymph nodes in their structure, which are found in the course of blood vessels. The afferent and efferent lymphatics are absent. Their sinuses are filled with blood rather than lymph. These are found in some animals in relation to their abdominal and thoracic viscera. Haemal nodes may represent an intermediate stage between a lymph node and the spleen. In man, the spleen is a large haemal node.

Haemolymph Nodes

In some animals, like sheep, haemolymph nodes have been described. Their structure is intermediate between lymph nodes and haemal nodes, having both lymphatic and vascular connections. Some observers regard them as stages in the transformation of lymph nodes to haemal nodes, but others do not believe even in their existence.

Mononuclear Phagocyte System or Macrophage System (Reticulo-endothelial System)

This system is closely related to lymphatic system because the two are independent structurally and functionally. The macrophage system is made up of highly phagocytic cells which are widely distributed in the body. These cells include : (a) macrophages of connective tissue, reticular tissue and lungs; (b) monocytes of blood; (c) Kupffer's cells of liver; (d) meningocytes of meninges; (e) microglial cells of nervous tissue; and (f) foreign body giant cells. The endothelial cells, fibroblasts, and most leucocytes are not included in this system because of their poor power of phagocytosis.

Functions : (1) The system forms first line of defence of the body against micro-organisms, because of the amoeboid and phagocytic properties of its cells; (2) the macrophages of lymphoid tissue are now considered to be intimately concerned with mounting specific immune responses by the neighbouring cells, and (3) many of the prominent sites of RES are also important sites of haemopoiesis.

Growth Pattern of Lymphoid Tissue

Lymphoid tissue of the body is prominent at birth, and grows rapidly during childhood. The growth ceases at about the time of puberty, and is followed by partial atrophy in the later years. This growth pattern is shared by lymph nodes, thymus, tonsils, lymphoid tissue of the intestines, and the follicles of spleen. However, the lymph nodes may enlarge again in response to inflammation (lymphadinitis) or tumour formation (Hodgkin's disease, lymphosarcoma, etc.). Lymph nodes are commonly enlarged by metastasis (spread) of the malignant growths (carcinoma).

Functions of Lymphoid System

1. Lymph capillaries absorb and remove the large protein molecules and other particulate matter from the tissue spaces. Thus the cellular debris and foreign particles (dust particles inhaled into the lungs, bacteria and other micro-organisms) are conveyed to the regional lymph nodes. Lymphatics (lacteals) help in transportation of fat from the gut.

2. Lymph nodes serve a number of functions.

    (a) They act as filters for the lymph which percolates slowly through the intricate network of its spaces. Thus the foreign particles are prevented from entering the bloodstream.

    (b) The foreign particles are engulfed by the macrophages in the sinuses.

    (c) Antigens are also trapped by the phagocytes.

    (d) The mature B-lymphocytes (plasma cells capable of producing antibodies) and mature T-lymphocytes are produced in the node.

    (e) Both the cellular and humoral immune responses are mounted against the antigen-laden phagocytes.

(f) The circulating lymphocytes can pass back into the lymphatic channels within the node.

(g) Humoral antibodies are freely produced by the lymph nodes.

3. Production (proliferation) and maturation of B- and T-lymphocytes is the main function of lymphoid tissue.

4. The additional functions of thymus and spleen are described in appropriate chapters.

Applied Anatomy of Lymphatic System

1. Lymphatics are primarily meant for coarse drainage, including cell debris and micro-organisms, from the tissue spaces to the regional lymph nodes, where the foreign and noxious material is filtered off by the phagocytic activity of the macrophage cells for its final disposal by the appropriate immune responses within the node. Thus the lymphatic system forms the first line of defence of the body.

While draining from an infected area, the lymphatics and lymph nodes carrying infected debris may become inflammed, resulting in *lymphangitis* and *lymphadinitis*. In acute cases the lymphatics are marked on the skin as painful red lines leading to the painful and tender swollen lymph nodes which may suppurate. Chronic infections (tuberculosis, syphilis, etc.) cause chronic lymphadinitis.

2. The filarial parasite lives in the lymphatics, which may become blocked, giving rise to solid oedema (elephantiasis) in the peripheral area of drainage. *Elephantiasis* is characterized by enormous enlargement of the part due to the thickened skin. The microfilariae enter the blood-stream only during night and, therefore, the blood for examination must be collected during night.

3. The lymphatics provide the most convenient *route of spread of the cancer cells*. Therefore, the lymphatic drainage of those organs which are commonly involved in cancer should be studied in greater details and with special interest for many reasons :

(a) it is helpful in the diagnosis of the primary site of the cancer;

(b) it helps in predicting the prognosis and in classifying the stage of cancer; and

(c) it helps the surgeon in doing the block dissections during operative removal of the cancer.

The spread of cancer causes enlargement of the regional lymph nodes, which become fixed and stony hard. Many a time the primary site of cancer is quite insignificant or even difficult to define, and the enormous enlargement of the draining lymph nodes due to secondary malignant deposits forms the most prominent part of the disease. A retrograde spread of cancer cells, after the blockage of lymphatics, may occur by a reversed flow of the lymph.

REFERENCES AND SUGGESTIONS FOR ADDITIONAL READING

Allen, L. (1967) Lymphatics and lymphoid tissue. *A. Rev. Physiol.*, 29 : 197-224.

Boggon, R.P. and Palfrey, A.J. (1973). The microscopic anatomy of human lymphatic trunks. *J. Anat.*, 114 : 389-405.

Jamieson, J.K. and Dobson, J.F. (1910). On the injection of lymphatics by Prussian blue. *J. Anat.*, 45 : 7-10; *Lancet*, 1 : 1061-1066, 1907; *Proc. R. Soc. Med.*, 2 : 149-174, 1908; *Lancet*, 1 : 493-495, 1910; *Br. J. Surg.*, 8 : 80-87, 1920.

Kinmonth, J.B. (1964). Some general aspects of the investigation and surgery of the lymphatic system. *J. Cardiovasc. Surg.*, 5 : 680-682.

Nopajaroonskri, C., Luk, S.C. and Simon. G.T. (1971). Ultrastructure of the normal lymph node. *Am. J. Path.*, 65 : 1-24.

Roitt, I.M. (1977). *Essential Immunology*, 3rd ed. Blackwell, Oxford.

Shridhar (1964). Roentgenographic visualization of human lymphatics, *J. Anat. Soc. India*, 13 : 15-17.

Steinman, R.M., Lustig, D.S. and Cohn, Z.A. (1974). Identification of a novel cell type in peripheral lymphoid organs of mice. II. Functional properties in vitro. *J. Exp. Med.*, 139 : 380-397.

William, P.L. and Warwick, R. (1980). *Gray's Anatomy*, 36th ed. Churchill Livingstone, London.

7

Nervous System

Nervous system is the chief controlling and coordinating system of the body. It controls and regulates all activities of the body, whether voluntary or involuntary, and adjusts the individual (organism) to the given surroundings. This is based on the special properties of sensitivity, conductivity and responsiveness of the nervous system.

The protoplasmic extensions of the nerve cells form the neural pathways called nerves. The nerves resemble the electricity wires. Like the electric current flowing through the wires, the impulses (sensory and motor) are conducted through the nerves. The sensory impulses are transmitted by the sensory (afferent) nerves from the periphery (skin, mucous membranes, muscles, tendons, joints, and special sense organs) to the central nervous system; the motor impulses are transmitted by the motor (efferent) nerves from the central nervous system to the periphery (muscles and glands). Thus the CNS is kept continuously informed about the surroundings (environment) through various sensory impulses, both general and special. The CNS in turn brings about necessary adjustment of the body by issuing appropriate orders which are passed on as motor impulses to the muscles, vessels, viscera and glands. The adjustment of the organism to the given surroundings is the most important function of the nervous system, without which it will not be possible for the organism to survive.

Parts of Nervous System

The nervous system is broadly divided into central and peripheral parts which are continuous with each other. Further subdivisions of each part are given below (Fig. 7.1).

A. **Central nervous system (CNS)** includes : (1) *Brain* or *encephalon*, which occupies cranial cavity, and contains the higher governing centres; and (2) *spinal cord* or *spinal medulla*, which occupies upper 2/3 of the vertebral canal, and contains many reflex centres.

B. **Peripheral nervous system (PNS)** is subdivided into the following two components. (1) *Cerebrospinal nervous system* is the somatic component of the peripheral nervous system, which includes 12 pairs of cranial nerves and 31 pairs of spinal nerves. It innervates the somatic structures of the head and neck, limbs and body wall, and mediates somatic sensory and motor functions. (2) *Peripheral autonomic nervous system* is the visceral component of the peripheral nervous system, which includes the visceral or splanchnic nerves that are connected to the CNS through the somatic nerves. It innervates the viscera, glands, blood vessels and nonstriated muscles, and mediates the visceral functions.

The cerebrospinal and autonomic nervous systems differ from each other in their efferent pathways. The somatic efferent pathway is made up of only one neuron which passes directly to the effector organs (skeletal muscles). However, the autonomic efferent pathway is made up of two neurons (preganglionic and postganglionic) with an intervening ganglion for the relay of the preganglionic fibres; the effector organs (viscera) are supplied by the postganglionic fibres. Thus, presence of a relay ganglion in the efferent pathway is a feature of the autonomic nervous system.

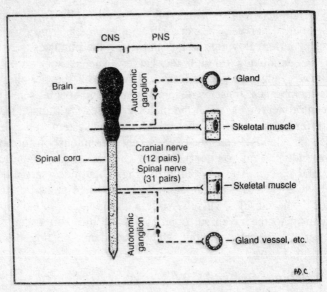

Fig. 7.1. Parts of the nervous system. In peripheral nervous system (PNS) the somatic component is shown with continuous lines, and the autonomic component with interrupted lines. CNS = central nervous system.

CELL TYPES OF NERVOUS SYSTEM

The nervous tissue is composed of two distinct types of cells :

(a) the excitable cells are the nerve cells or neurons; and

(b) the non-excitable cells constitute neuroglia and ependyma in the CNS, and Schwann cells in the PNS.

1. Neuron

Each nerve cell or neuron (Fig. 7.2) has :

(a) a cell body or *soma* or *perikaryon*, having a central nucleus and Nissl granules in its cytoplasm; and

(b) cell processes called neurites, which are of two types. Many short afferent processes, which are freely branching and varicose, are called *dendrites*. A single long efferent process, which may give off occasional branches (collaterals) and is of uniform diameter, is called *axon*. The terminal branches of the axon are called axon terminals or telodendria. The cell bodies (somata) of the neurons form grey matter and nuclei in the CNS, and ganglia in the PNS. The cell processes (axons) form tracts in the CNS, and nerves in the PNS.

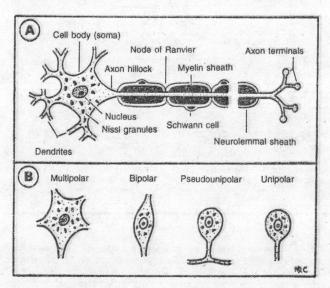

Fig. 7.2. (A) Parts of a neuron. (B) Types of neurons.

Types of neurons. Neurons can be classified in several ways. According to the number of their processes (neurites) they may be :

(a) *unipolar*, e.g., mesencephalic nucleus;

(b) *pseudo-unipolar*, e.g. sensory ganglia;

(c) *bipolar*, e.g., spiral and vestibular ganglia; and

(d) *multipolar*, the most common type.

According to the length of axon, the neurons are classified as

(i) *Golgi type I* neurons, with a long axon; and

(ii) *Golgi type II* neurons (microneurons), with a short or no axon.

Dynamic polarity. The neurons show dynamic polarity in their processes. The impulse flows towards the soma in the dendrites, and away from the soma in the axon. However, in certain microneurons, where the axon is absent, the impulse can flow in either direction through their dendrites.

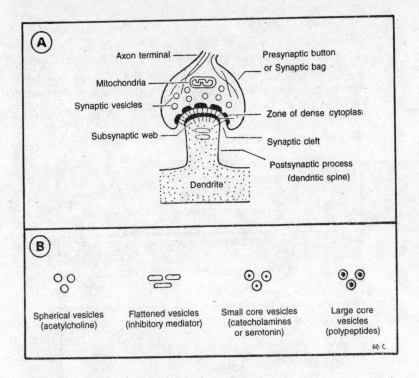

Fig. 7.3. (A) Fine structure of an axo-dendritic synapse. The synaptic bag contains vesicles filled with the chemical neurotransmitter. Spherical vesicles contain acetylcholine (excitatory), flattened vesicles contain inhibitory mediator, small dense core vesicles contain catecholamines or serotonin, and large core vesicles contain polypeptides. In synapses without vesicles (gap junctions) the conduction electrical. (B) Types of the synaptic vesicles.

Synapse. The neurons form long chains along which the impulses are conducted in different directions. Each junction between the neurons is called a synapse (Fig. 7.3). It is important to know that the contact between the neurons is by contiguity and not by continuity (neuron theory of Waldeyer, 1891), and the impulse is transmitted across a synapse by specific neurotransmitters, like acetylcholine, catecholamines (noradrenalin and dopamine), serotonin, histamine, glycine, GABA, and certain polypeptides. The most common types of the synapse are axo-dendritic, somato-somatic, somato-dendritic, or serial in nature. In synaptic glomeruli groups of axons make contact with the dendrites of one or more neurons for complex interactions. Functionally, a synapse may either be inhibitory or excitatory.

2. Neuroglia

The non-excitable supporting cells of the nervous system form a major component of the nervous tissue. These cells include :

1. *neuroglial cells*, found in the parenchyma of brain and spinal cord;

2. *ependymal cells* lining the internal cavities;

3. *capsular* or *satellite cells*, surrounding neurons of the sensory and autonomic ganglia;

4. *Schwann cells*, forming sheaths for axons of peripheral nerves;

5. several types of *supporting cells*, ensheathing the motor and sensory nerve terminals, and supporting the sensory epithelia.

The neuroglial cells, found in the parenchyma of brain and spinal cord, are broadly classified as :

(A) *macroglia*, of ectodermal (neural plate) origin, comprising astrocytes, oligodendrocytes, and glioblasts; and

(B) *microglia*, of mesodermal origin. All glial cells are much smaller but far more numerous than the nerve cells.

(a) **Astrocytes.** As the name suggests these cells are star-shaped because of their numerous processes radiating in all directions. Astrocytes are of two types. *Protoplasmic astrocytes*, with thick and symmetrical processes are found in the grey matter. *Fibrous astrocytes*, with thin and asymmetrical processes, are found in the white matter. The processes of astrocytes often end in plate-like expansions on the blood vessels, ependyma, and pial surface of the CNS. The functions of various glial cells are enumerated below.

(b) **Oligodendrocytes.** As the name suggests these cells have fewer cell processes. According to their distribution, the oligodendrocytes may be intrafascicular, or perineuronal. The *intrafascicular cells* are found in the myelinated tracts, whereas the *perineuronal cells* on the surface of the somata of neurons.

(c) **Glioblasts.** These are stem cells which can differentiate into macroglial cells. They are particularly numerous beneath the ependyma.

(d) **Microglia.** These are the smallest of the glial cells which have a flattened cell body with a few short, fine processes. They are often related to capillaries, and are said to be phagocytic in nature. Microglial cells are possibly derived from the circulating monocytes which migrate into the CNS during the late foetal and early postnatal life.

Functions of Glial and Ependymal Cells

1. They provide mechanical support to neurons.

2. Because of their non-conducting nature, the glial cells act as insulators between the neurons and prevent neuronal impulses from spreading in unwanted directions.

3. They can remove the foreign material and cell debris by phagocytosis.

4. They can repair the damaged areas of nervous tissue. By proliferation (gliosis) they form glial scar tissue, and fill the gaps left by degenerated neurons.

5. Glial cells can take up and store neurotransmitters released by the neighbouring synapses. These can either be metabolized or released again from the glial cells.

6. They help in neuronal functions by maintaining a suitable metabolic and ionic environment for the neurons.

7. Oligodendrocytes myelinate tracts.

8. Ependymal cells are concerned with exchanges of materials between brain and CSF.

9. The role of glial cells in the nutrition of nerve cells is claimed since long but is not confirmed.

BLOOD-BRAIN BARRIER

Certain dyes, when injected intravenously, fail to stain the parenchyma of brain and spinal cord, although they pass easily into the non-nervous tissues. However, the same dyes, when injected into the ventricles, enter the brain substances easily. This indicates that a barrier exists at the capillary level between the blood and nerve cells. The possible structures constituting the blood-brain barrier are :

(a) capillary endothelium without fenestrations;

(b) basement membrane of the endothelium; and

(c) the end feet of astrocytes covering the capillary walls.

The barrier permits a selective passage of blood contents to the nervous tissue, and thus the toxic and harmful substances are ordinarily prevented from reaching the brain.

REFLEX ARC

A reflex arc is the basic functional unit of the nervous system, which can perform an integrated neural activity. In its simplest form (monosynaptic reflex arc—Fig. 7.4), it is made up of (Fig. 7.5) :

(a) a receptor, e.g., skin;

(b) a sensory or afferent neuron;

(c) a motor or efferent neuron; and

(d) an effector, e.g., muscle.

The complex forms of reflex arc are polysynaptic due to addition of one or more internuncial neurons (interneurons) in between the afferent and efferent neurons.

An involuntary motor response of the body is called a reflex action. The stretch reflexes (tendon jerks) are the examples of monosynaptic reflexes, whereas the withdrawal reflex (response to a painful stimulus) is a polysynaptic reflex.

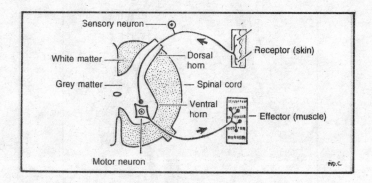

Fig. 7.4. A monosynaptic reflex arc. Arrows indicate the direction of conduction of the impulse.

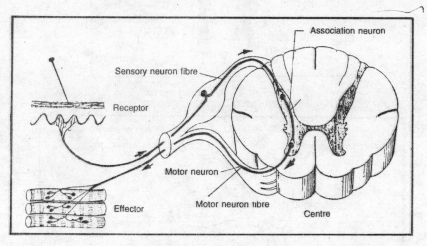

Fig. 7.5. Components of a reflex arc.

PERIPHERAL NERVES

The nerves are solid white cords composed of bundles (fasciculi) of nerve fibres. Each nerve fibre is an axon with its coverings. The nerve fibres are supported and bound together by connective tissue sheaths at different

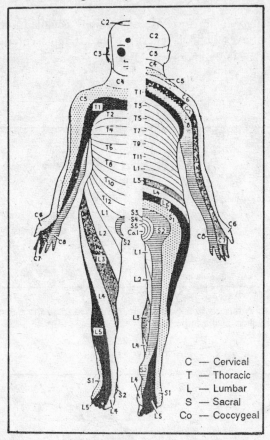

C — Cervical
T — Thoracic
L — Lumbar
S — Sacral
Co — Coccygeal

Fig. 7.6. Typical spinal nerve.

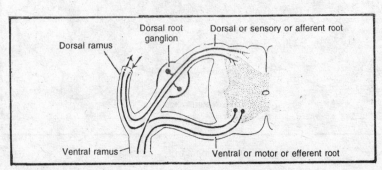

Dorsal root ganglion

Dorsal or sensory or afferent root

Dorsal ramus

Ventral ramus

Ventral or motor or efferent root

Fig. 7.7. Formation of brachial plexus.

levels of organization of the nerve. The whole nerve trunk is ensheathed by epineurium, each fasciculus by perineurium, and each nerve fibre by a delicate endoneurium. The toughness of a nerve is due to its fibrous sheaths, otherwise the nerve tissue itself is very delicate and friable.

SPINAL NERVES

There are 31 pairs of spinal nerves, including 8 cervical, 12 thoracic, 5 lumbar, 5 sacral, and 1 coccygeal. Area of skin supplied by a single segment of spinal cord is called a dermatome (Fig. 7.6). Each spinal nerve is connected with the spinal cord by two roots, a *ventral root* which is motor, and a *dorsal root* which is sensory (Fig. 7.7). The dorsal root is characterized by the presence of a *spinal ganglion* at its distal end (Fig. 7.8). In the majority of nerves the ganglion lies in the intervertebral foramen.

The ventral and dorsal nerve roots unite together within the intervertebral foramen to form the *spinal nerve*. The nerve emerges through the intervertebral foramen, gives off recurrent meningeal branches, and then divides immediately into a *dorsal* and a *ventral ramus*.

The *dorsal ramus* passes backwards and supplies the intrinsic muscles of the back, and the skin covering them.

The *ventral ramus* is connected with the sympathetic ganglion, and is distributed to the limb or the anterolateral body wall. In case of a typical (thoracic) spinal nerve, the ventral ramus does not mix with neighbouring rami, and gives off several muscular branches, a lateral cutaneous branch, and an anterior cutaneous branch. However, the ventral rami, of other spinal nerves are plaited to form the nerve plexuses for the limbs, like the brachial plexus, lumbar plexus, etc.

Nerve Plexuses for Limbs (Fig. 7.9)

All nerve plexuses are formed only by the ventral rami, and never by the dorsal rami. They supply the limbs. Against each plexus the spinal cord is enlarged to form 'cervical enlargement' for the brachial plexus, and 'lumbar enlargement' for the lumbosacral plexus.

Each nerve root of the plexus (ventral ramus) divides into a ventral, a dorsal division. The ventral division supplies the flexor compartment, and the dorsal division, the extensor compartment, of the limb. The flexor compartment has a richer nerve supply than the extensor compartment. The flexor skin is more sensitive than the extensor skin, and the flexor muscles (antigravity, bulkier muscles) are more efficient and are under a more precise control than the coarse extensor muscles.

The plexus formation is a physiological or functional adaptation, and is perhaps the result of the following special features in the limbs :

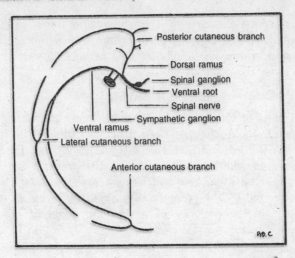

Fig. 7.8. Formation, course and branches of a typical spinal nerve.

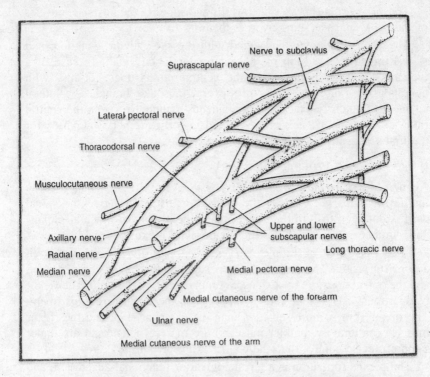

Fig. 7.9. Scheme to show stages of formation of brachial plexus.

1. overlapping of dermatomes;
2. overlapping of myotomes;
3. composite nature of muscles;
4. possible migration of muscles from the trunk to the limbs; and
5. linkage of the opposite groups of muscles in the spinal cord for reciprocal innervation.

Blood and Nerve Supply of Peripheral Nerves

The peripheral nerves are supplied by vessels, called *vasa nervorum*, which form longitudinal anastomoses on the surface of the nerves. The nerves distributed to the sheaths of the nerve trunks are called *nervi nervorum*.

NERVE FIBRES

Each nerve fibre is an axon with its coverings. Larger axons are covered by a myelin sheath and are termed *myelinated* or *medullated fibres*. The fatty nature of myelin is responsible for the glistening whiteness of the peripheral nerve trunks (and white matter of the CNS). Thinner axons, of less than one micron diameter, do not have the myelin sheath and are therefore termed *non-myelinated, non-medullated* or *grey fibres*. However, all the fibres whether myelinated or non-myelinated have a neurolemmal sheath, which is uniformly absent in the tracts. In peripheral nerves, both the myelin and neurolemmal sheaths are derived from Schwann cells.

Myelinated Fibres

Myelinated fibres form the bulk of the somatic nerves. Structurally, they are made up of following parts (Fig. 7.10) from within outwards.

1. *Axis cylinder* forms the central core of the fibre. It consists of axoplasm covered by axolemma.
2. *Myelin sheath*, derived from Schwann cells, surrounds the axis cylinder. It is made up of alternate concentric layers of lipids and proteins formed by spiralization of the mesaxon; the lipids include cholesterol, glycolipids and phospholipids. Myelin sheath is interrupted at regular intervals called the *nodes of Ranvier* where the adjacent Schwann cells meet. Collateral branches of the axon arise at the nodes of Ranvier. Thicker axons possess a thicker coat of myelin and longer internodes. Each *internode* is myelinated by one Schwann cell. Oblique clefts in the myelin, called *incisures of Schmidt Lanterman*, provide conduction channels for metabolites into the depth of the myelin and to the subjacent axon. Myelin sheath acts as an insulator for the nerve fibres.

3. *Neurolemmal sheath* (sheath of Schwann) surrounds the myelin sheath. It represents the plasma membrane (basal lamina) of the Schwann cell. Beneath the membrane there lies a thin layer of cytoplasm with the nucleus of the Schwann cell. The sheaths of two cells interdigitate at the nodes of Ranvier. Neurolemmal sheath is necessary for regeneration of a damaged nerve. Tracts do not regenerate because of its absence.

4. *Endoneurium* is a delicate connective tissue sheath which surrounds the neurolemmal sheath.

Non-Myelinated Fibres

Non-myelinated fibres comprise the smaller axons of the CNS, in addition to peripheral postganglionic autonomic fibres, several types of fine sensory fibres (C fibres of skin, muscle and viscera), olfactory nerves, etc. Structurally, a non-myelinated 'fibre' consists of a group of small axons (0.12-2 microns diameter) that have invaginated separately a single Schwann cell (in series) without any spiralling of the mesaxon (Fig. 7.10). The endoneurium, instead of ensheathing individual axons, surrounds all the neurolemmal sheath by virtue of which the non-myelinated fibres, like the myelinated fibres, can regenerate after damage.

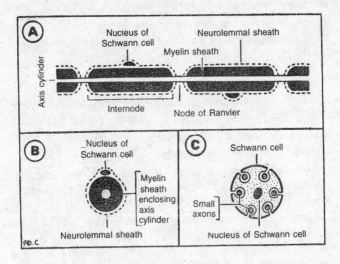

Fig. 7.10. (A) Structure of a myelinated nerve fibre. (B) Transverse section of the non-myelinated nerve fibres.

Classification of Peripheral Nerve Fibres

A. **According to their function**, the nerve fibres may be :

1. *somatic efferent*, to supply striated muscles of somatic origin;

2. *general visceral efferent* to supply smooth muscles and glands;

3. *special visceral efferent* (*branchial efferent*) to supply striated muscles of branchial origin;

4. *general somatic afferent*, to carry exteroceptive impulses from the skin, and proprioceptive impulses from the muscles, tendons and joints;

5. *general visceral afferent*, to carry visceroceptive impulses (like pain) from the viscera;

6. *special visceral afferent*, to carry the sensation of taste; and

7. special somatic afferent to carry the sensations of smell, vision, hearing and equilibrium.

B. **According to their size and speed of conduction**, the nerve fibres are divided into three categories, namely A, B and C.

1. *Group A fibres* (thickest and fastest) are myelinated 1.5-22 microns in diameter, with a conduction speed of 4-120 metres per second. Examples : skeletomotor fibres (alpha A), fusimotor fibres (beta A and gamma A), and afferent fibres to skin, muscles and tendons.

2. *Group B fibres* (medium size and speed) and myelinated, 1.5-3 microns in diameter, with a conduction speed of 3-15 metres per second. Example : preganglionic autonomic efferents.

3. *Group C fibres* (thinnest and slowest) are non-myelinated, 0.1-2 microns in diameter, with a conduction speed of 0.5-4 metres per second. Examples : postganglionic autonomic efferents, and afferent fibres to skin, muscles and viscera. The same efferents with a conduction speed and myelination similar to B fibres are called delta A fibres. Thus the fibre diameter is directly proportional to conduction velocity; the velocity (in metres per second) is approximately six times the diameter (in microns).

Degeneration and Regeneration of Neurons

If a nerve (axons) is injured or cut a series of degenerative and then regenerative changes follow. The degenerative changes in the neurons occur both proximal (*retrograde degeneration*) and distal (*antegrade degeneration*) to the site of injury.

1. The *cell bodies* undergo *chromatolysis* within 48 hours of injury. The cell becomes swollen and rounded, nucleus is pushed to the periphery, and the Nissl granules disintegrate and disappear.

2. The *proximal part of the axon* survives if the mother cells do not die. Only a small segment near the cut end degenerates in a way similar to the distal part.

3. At the *site of injury*, the Schwann cells proliferate more actively in the distal stump than in the proximal, in an attempt to fill the gap. Gaps up to 3 cm may be bridged in this way. Bridging can be facilitated by stitching the two stumps. However, in wider gaps nerve grafts may be tried.

4. The *distal part of the axons* undergoes *Wallerian (antegrade) degeneration* within a few days of injury. The axis cylinder becomes fragmented and the myelin sheath breaks up into fat droplets. The Schwann cells multiply, which on one hand act as macrophages to remove the debris of degenerated axon and myelin, and on the other hand form a large series of membranous (neurolemmal) tubes which play a vital role in regeneration of the nerve fibres. The nucleated cellular cords in the distal stump are called *bands of Bungner*.

During **regeneration** the tip of the surviving (proximal) axon shows an active growth. It forms a terminal swelling from the surface of which many small axonal sprouts develop which grow in the surrounding tissues in an effort to reach the endoneurial tubes of the distal segment. One of the axonal sprouts which succeeds in reaching the endoneurial tube survives and grows rapidly (1-2 mm per day) due to the *contact guidance* between the growing tip of the axon and the Schwann cell surfaces within the endoneurial tube. The other axonal sprouts which fail to reach any tube degenerate and disappear. When the growing axon tip reaches and reinnervates the peripheral end organ the surrounding Schwann cells lay down myelin sheath with appropriate nodes of Ranvier and incisures of Schmidt-Lanterman. The role of neurolemmal sheaths within the endoneurial tubes as a guiding factor to the regenerating proximal axon is considered of paramount importance. Thus a nerve can regenerate because it has a neurolemmal sheath, but a tract cannot regenerate because it has no such sheath. However, a tract after demyelination can remyelinate, as is seen in demyelinating diseases.

AUTONOMIC NERVOUS SYSTEM

Autonomic nervous system controls involuntary activities of the body, like sweating, salivation, peristalsis, etc. It differs fundamentally from the somatic nervous system in having : (a) the preganglionic fibres arising from the CNS; (b) the ganglia for relay of the preganglionic fibres; and (c) the postganglionic fibres arising from the ganglia which supply the effectors (smooth muscles and glands). In contrast, the somatic nerves after arising from the CNS reach their destination without any interruption.

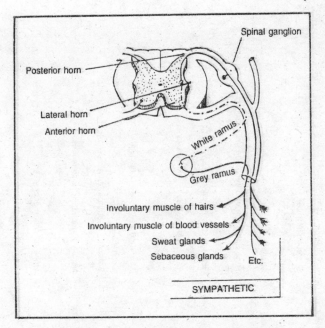

Fig. 7.11. Plan of sympathetic nervous system.

Autonomic nervous system is divided into two more or less complementary parts, the sympathetic and parasympathetic systems. The sympathetic activities are widespread and diffused, and combat the acute emergencies. The parasympathetic activities are usually discrete and isolated, and combat the long term emergencies. Both systems function in absolute coordination and adjust the body involuntarily to the given surroundings.

SYMPATHETIC NERVOUS SYSTEM

1. It is also known as 'thoracolumbar' outflow because it arises from T1 to L2 segments of the spinal cord.

2. The medullated preganglionic fibres (*white rami communicantes*) arise from the lateral column of the spinal cord, emerge through the ventral rami where the white rami are connected to the ganglia of the sympathetic chain (Fig. 7.11).

3. Preganglionic fibres relay either in the *lateral ganglia* (sympathetic chain) or in the *collateral ganglia*, e.g., the coeliac ganglion. The non-medullated post-ganglionic fibres (*grey rami communicantes*) run for some distance before reaching the organ of supply. The adrenal medulla is a unique exception in the body; it is supplied by the preganglionic fibres.

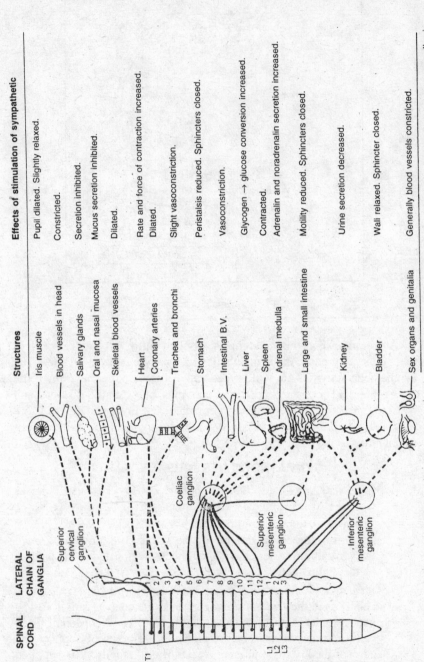

Structures	Effects of stimulation of sympathetic
Iris muscle	Pupil dilated. Slightly relaxed.
Blood vessels in head	Constricted.
Salivary glands	Secretion inhibited.
Oral and nasal mucosa	Mucus secretion inhibited.
Skeletal blood vessels	Dilated.
Heart	Rate and force of contraction increased.
Coronary arteries	Dilated.
Trachea and bronchi	Slight vasoconstriction.
Stomach	Peristalsis reduced. Sphincters closed.
Intestinal B.V.	Vasoconstriction.
Liver	Glycogen → glucose conversion increased.
Spleen	Contracted.
Adrenal medulla	Adrenalin and noradrenalin secretion increased.
Large and small intestine	Motility reduced. Sphincters closed.
Kidney	Urine secretion decreased.
Bladder	Wall relaxed. Sphincter closed.
Sex organs and genitalia	Generally blood vessels constricted.

Fig. 7.12A. The sympathetic outflow, the main structures supplied and the effects of stimulation. Solid lines — preganglionic

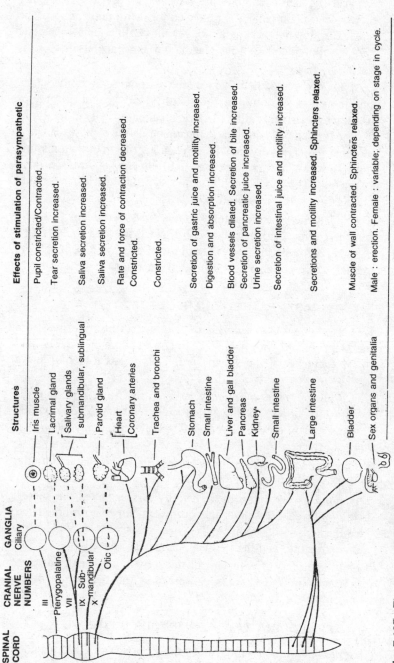

SPINAL CORD	CRANIAL NERVE NUMBERS	GANGLIA	Structures	Effects of stimulation of parasympathetic
	III	Ciliary	Iris muscle	Pupil constricted/Contracted.
	Pterygopalatine		Lacrimal gland	Tear secretion increased.
	VII		Salivary glands submandibular, sublingual	Saliva secretion increased.
	IX Sub-mandibular	Otic	Parotid gland	Saliva secretion increased.
	X		Heart	Rate and force of contraction decreased.
			Coronary arteries	Constricted.
			Trachea and bronchi	Constricted.
			Stomach	Secretion of gastric juice and motility increased.
			Small intestine	Digestion and absorption increased.
			Liver and gall bladder	Blood vessels dilated. Secretion of bile increased.
			Pancreas	Secretion of pancreatic juice increased.
			Kidney	Urine secretion increased.
			Small intestine	Secretion of intestinal juice and motility increased.
			Large intestine	Secretions and motility increased. Sphincters relaxed.
			Bladder	Muscle of wall contracted. Sphincters relaxed.
			Sex organs and genitalia	Male : erection. Female : variable; depending on stage in cycle.

Fig. 7.12B. The parasympathetic outflow, the main structures supplied and the effects of stimulation. Solid lines — preganglionic fibres; broken lines — postganglionic fibres. Where there are no broken lines, the 2nd neurone is in the wall of the structure.

4. Sympathetic nerve endings are *adrenergic* in nature, meaning thereby that noradrenalin is produced for neurotransmission. The only exception to this general rule are the cholinergic sympathetic nerves supplying the sweat glands and skeletal muscle vessels for vasodilatation.

5. *Functionally*, sympathetic nerves are vasomotor (vasoconstrictor), sudomotor (secretomotor to sweat glands), and pilomotor (contract the arrector pili and cause erection of hair) in the limbs and body wall. In addition, sympathetic activity causes dilation of pupil, pale face, dry mouth, tachycardia, rise in blood pressure, inhibition of hollow viscera, and closure of the perineal sphincters. The blood supply to the skeletal muscles, heart and brain is markedly increased (Fig. 7.12A).

Thus, sympathetic reactions tend to be 'mass reactions', widely diffused in their effect and that they are directed towards mobilization of the resources of the body for expenditure of energy in dealing with the emergencies or emotional crises (fear, fight, flight).

PARASYMPATHETIC NERVOUS SYSTEM

1. It is also known as *'craniosacral' outflow* because it arises from the brain (mixed with 3rd, 7th, 9th and 10th cranial nerves) and S 2-4 segments of the spinal cord. Thus it has a cranial and a sacral part.

2. The *preganglionic fibres* are very long, reaching right upto the viscera of supply. The ganglia, called *terminal ganglia*, are situated mostly on the viscera and, therefore, the *postganglionic fibres* are very short.

3. Parasympathetic nerve endings are *cholinergic* in nature, similar to the somatic nerves.

4. *Functionally*, parasympathetic activity is seen when the subject is fully relaxed. His pupils are constricted, lenses accommodated, face flushed, mouth moist, pulse slow, pressure low, bladder and gut contracting, and the perineal sphincters relaxed (Fig. 7.12B).

In general the effects of parasympathetic activity are usually discrete and isolated, and directed towards conservation and restoration of the resources of energy in the body.

APPLIED ANATOMY OF NERVOUS SYSTEM

1. *Irritation* of a motor nerve causes muscular spasm. Mild irritation of a sensory nerve causes tingling and numbness, but when severe

it causes pain along the distribution of the nerve. Irritation of a mixed nerve causes combined effects.

2. *Damage* to a motor nerve causes muscular paralysis, and damage to a sensory nerve causes localized anaesthesia and analgesia. Damage to a mixed nerve gives rise to both the sensory and motor losses.

Regeneration of a damaged nerve depends on the degree of injury, particularly on the continuity of the nerve. Different degrees of nerve injury are expressed by the following three terms.

(a) *Neurapraxia* is a minimal lesion causing transient functional block without any degeneration. Recovery is spontaneous and complete.

(b) *Axonotmesis* is a lesion where, although continuity is preserved, true Wallerian degeneration occurs. Regeneration takes place in due course of its own.

(c) *Neurotmesis* is the complete division of a nerve. For regeneration to occur the cut ends must be sutured.

3. Severe pain along the distribution of a nerve is called *neuralgia*. *Neuropathy* is a broad term used for any disease of the nervous system (often a degenerative disease). Inflammation of a nerve is marked by neuralgia with sensory and motor deficits, and is called *neuritis*.

4. *Denervation* of a part produces *trophic changes*. The skin becomes dry (no sweating), smooth (loss of hair) and glazed; trophic ulcers may develop which do not heal easily. In patients with leprosy, repeated painless injuries to the tips of the fingers and toes makes them worn out and blunted.

A joint after denervation becomes a *neuropathic (Charcot's) joint*, which shows painless swelling; excessive mobility and bony destruction. The common medical diseases associated with trophic changes are leprosy, tabes dorsalis, and syringomyelia. The bed sores in paralysed patients are examples of the trophic ulcers. In general the ulcers and wounds in the denervated skin do not heal easily.

REFERENCES AND SUGGESTIONS
FOR ADDITIONAL READING

Glees, P. and Hasan, M. (1976). *Lipofuscin in Neuronal Aging and Diseases*. Georg Thieme Verlag, Stuttgart.

Glees, P., Hasan, M. and Tischner. K. (1966). Trans-synaptic atrophy in the lateral geniculate body of the monkeys. *J. Physiol. (Lond.)* 188 : 17-19.

Grey, E.G. Morphology of synapses. *J. Anat.*, 93 : 420-423, 1959; *J. Anat.*, 95 : 345-356, 1961; *Prog. Brain Res.*, 31 : 141-155, 1969; In : *Essays on the Nervous System* (Bellairs. R. and Gray, E.G., eds.). Clarendon Press, Oxford, 1974.

Gregson, N.A. (1975). The chemistry of myelin. In : *The Peripheral Nerve* (London, D.N., ed.). Chapman & Hall, London.

Hasan, M., Glees, P. and Tischner, K. (1967). Electron microscopic observations on myelin degeneration in the lateral geniculate body of blinded monkeys. *J. Anat. Soc. India*, 16 : 1-11.

Hasan, M., and Glees, P. (1972). Oligodendrocytes in the normal and chronically de-afferented lateral geniculate body of the monkeys. *Z. Zellforsch.*, 135 : 115-127.

Hasan, M., and Glees, P. (1972). Electron microscopic appearance of neuronal lipofuscin using different preparative techniques freeze-etching. *Exp. Geront.*, 7 : 345-351.

Hasan, M. and Glees, P. (1972). Genesis and possible dissolution of neuronal lipofuscin. *Gerontologia*, 18 : 217-236.

Hasan, M. and Glees, P. (1974). Electron microscopic study of the changes in fibrous astrocytes of the lateral geniculate body of blinded monkeys. *J. Anat. Soc. India*, 23 : 1-4.

Hasan, M., Shipstone, A.C. and Bajpai, V.K. (1978). Scanning electron microscopy of ventricular ependyma. *Bull. Electron Microscopic Soc. India*, 2 : 1-2.

Jacobs, S. and Jacob, M. (1971). Intersegmental anastomoses between adjacent dorsal roots of spinal cord in the human. *Neurol. India*, 19 : 51-54.

Jacob, M. and Weddell, G. (1975). Neural intersegmental connections in the spinal roots and ganglion region of the rat. *J. Comp. Neurol.*, 161 : 115-123.

Linge, E.A. et al., (1973). Identification of glial cells in the brain of young rats. *J. Comp. Neurol.*, 146 : 43-72.

Palay, S.L. and Chan Palay, V. (1977). General morphology of neurons and neuroglia. In : *Handbook of Physiology* (Kandel, E.R., ed.), Vol. 1, Part 2. Physiological Society, Bethesda.

Shepherd, G.M. (1974). *The Synaptic Organization of the Brain.* Oxford University Press, New York.

Singh, I. (1982). *A Textbook of Human Neuroanatomy.* Vikas, New Delhi.

Varon, S. and Bunge, R.P. (1978). Trophic mechanisms in the peripheral nervous system. *Ann. Rev. Neurosci.*, 1 : 327-361.

Williams, P.L. and Hall, S.M. (1971). Prolonged in vivo observations of normal peripheral nerve fibres and their acute reactions to crush and local trauma. *J. Anat.*, 108 : 397-408.

8

Skin and Fasciae

1. SKIN

Synonyms

1. Cutis (L); 2. Derma (G); 3. Integument. Compare with the terms cutaneous, dermatology and dermatomes.

Definition

Skin is the general covering of the entire external surface of the body, including the external auditory meatus and the outer surface of tymphanic membrane. It is continuous with the mucous membrane at the orifices of the body. Because of a large number of its functions the skin is regarded as an important organ of the body.

Surface Area

In an adult the surface area of the skin is 1.5-2(1.7) sq. metres. In order to assess the area involved in burns, one can follow the rule of nine : head and neck, 9%; each upper limb, 9%; the front of the trunk, the back of the trunk (including buttocks), and each lower limb, 18% each; and perineum, 1%.

The surface area of an individual can be calculated by Du Bois formula. Thus, $A = W \times H \times 71.84$, where A = surface area in sq. cm, W = weight in kg, and H = height in cm.

Pigmentation of Skin

The colour of the skin is determined by at least five pigments present at different levels and places of the skin. These are :

1. *melanin*, brown in colour, present in the germinative zone of the epidermis;
2. *melanoid*, resembles melanin, present diffusely throughout the epidermis;

3. *carotene*, yellow to orange in colour, present in stratum corneum and the fat cells of dermis and superficial fascia;

4. *haemoglobin* (purple); and

5. *oxyhaemoglobin* (red), present in the cutaneous vessels.

The amounts of first three pigments vary with the race, age, and part of the body. In white races, the colour of the skin depends chiefly on the vascularity of the dermis and thickness (translucency) of the keratin. The colour is red where keratin is thin (lips), and it is white where keratin is thick (palms and soles).

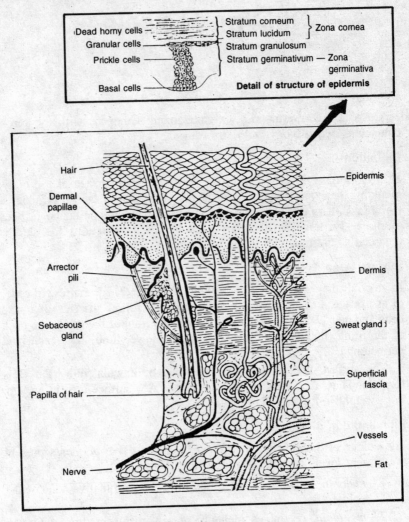

Fig. 8.1. Section of thick skin.

Thickness

The thickness of the skin varies from about 0.5 to 3 mm.

Structure of Skin (Fig. 8.1A & B)

The skin is composed of two distinct layers, epidermis and dermis.

A. **Epidermis** (Fig. 8.1A & B) is the superficial, avascular layer of stratified squamous epithelium. It is ectodermal in origin and gives rise to the appendages of the skin, namely hair, nails, sweat glands and sebaceous glands. Structurally, the epidermis is made up of a superficial *cornified zone* and a deep *germinative zone*. The cornified zone includes three strata of cells, namely stratum corneum, stratum lucidum and stratum granulosum, from superficial to the deeper plane in that order. The germinative zone, similarly, includes two strata, namely stratum spinosum of polyhedral cells, and stratum basale (stratum germinativum or Malpighian layer) of a single layer of columnar cells. The cells of the deepest layer proliferate and pass towards the surface to replace the cornified cells lost due to wear and tear. As the cells migrate superficially, they become more and more flattened, and lose their nuclei to form the flattened dead cells of the stratum corneum. In the stratum basale, there are also 'dopa' positive *melanocytes* (melanoblasts, dendritic cells, or clear cells) of neural crest origin, which synthesize melanin.

B. **Dermis** or **corium** is the deep, vascular layer of the skin, derived from mesoderm. It is made up of connective tissue (with variable elastic fibres) mixed with blood vessels, lymphatics and nerves. The connective tissue is arranged into a superficial *papillary layer* and a deep *reticular layer*. The papillary layer forms conical, blunt projections (dermal papillae) which fit into reciprocal depressions on the undersurface of the epidermis. The reticular layer is composed chiefly of the white fibrous tissue arranged mostly in parallel bundles. The direction of the bundles, constituting *cleavage lines* (Langer's lines), is longitudinal in the limbs and horizontal in the trunk and neck. In old age the elastic fibres atrophy and the skin becomes wrinkled. Overstretching of the skin may lead to

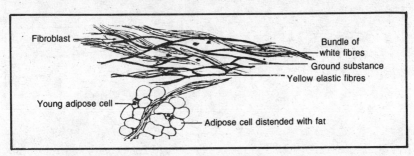

Fig. 8.2. Connective tissue from dermis and subcutaneous layer.

rupture of the fibres, followed by scar formation. These scars appear as white streaks on the skin (e.g., lineae gravidarum). At the *flexure lines* of the joints, the skin is firmly adherent to the underlying deep fascia. Dermis is the real skin, because, when dried it makes greenhide, and when tanned it makes leather. Its deep surface is continuous with the superficial fascia (Fig. 8.2).

Surface Irregularities of the Skin

The skin is marked by three types of surface irregularities, the tension lines, flexure lines and papillary ridges (Montagna and Lobitz, 1964).

1. **Tension lines** form a network of linear furrows which divide the surface into polygonal or lozenge-shaped areas. These lines to some extent correspond to variations in the pattern of fibres in the dermis.

2. **Flexure lines** (**skin creases** or **skin joints**) are certain permanent lines along which the skin folds during habitual movements (chiefly flexion) of the joints. The skin along these lines is thin and firmly bound to the deep fascia. The lines are prominent opposite the flexure of the joints, particularly on the palms, soles and digits.

3. **Papillary ridges** (**friction ridges**) are confined to palms and soles and their digits. They form narrow ridges separated by fine parallel grooves, arranged in curved arrays. They correspond to patterns of dermal papillae. Their study constitutes a branch of science, called dermato-glyphics (Cummins and Midlo, 1961). Three major patterns in the human fingerprints include loops, whorls and arches. These patterns and many other minor features are determined genetically by multifactorial inheritance.

APPENDAGES OF SKIN

1. Nails (Fig. 8.3)

Synonyms. (a) Onych or onycho (G); and (b) ungues (L). Compare with the terms paronychia, koilonychia and onychomycosis.

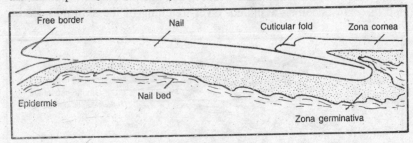

Fig. 8.3. Nail — L.S.

Nails are hardened keratin plates (cornified zone) on the dorsal surface of the tips of fingers and toes, acting as a rigid support for the digital pads of terminal phalanges. Each nail has following parts. (a) *Root* is the proximal hidden part which is burried into the nail groove and is overlapped by the nail fold of the skin. (b) *Free border* is the distal part free from the skin. (c) *Body* is the exposed part of the nail which is adherent to the underlying skin. The proximal part of the body presents a white opaque crescent called *lunule*. Each lateral border of the nail body is overlapped by a fold of a skin, termed the *nail wall*. The skin (germinative zone + corium) beneath the root and body of the nail is called *nail bed*. The germinative zone of the nail bed beneath the root and lunule is thick and proliferative (germinal matrix), and is responsible for the growth of the nail. The rest of the nail bed is thin (sterile matrix) over which the growing nail glides.

Under the translucent body (except lunule) of the nail the corium is very vascular. This accounts for their pink colour. In anaemia the nails are pale and white. In iron deficiency anaemia the nails become thin, brittle and spoon-shaped (koilonychia).

Hypertrophy of the nail bed (*clubbing*) occurs in chronic suppurative disease (lung abscess, bronchiectasis, osteomyelitis) and in severe type of cyanosis (Fallot's tetralogy, chronic CCF).

Disturbances of nail growth due to acute illness or trauma give rise to transverse grooves in the nail substance, which move distally with the nail growth. Since the average rate of growth is about 0.1 mm per day or 3 mm per month, the date of the past illness can be estimated.

It takes about 90-120 days for the whole nail (body) to grow. Therefore, in fungal diseases of the nails the course of treatment should last for not less than this period. The growth is faster in summer than in winter, in the fingers than in toes, and in the longer fingers than in the shorter ones.

2. Hairs (Fig. 8.4)

Hairs are keratinous filaments derived from invaginations of the germinative layer of epidermis into the dermis. These are peculiar to mammals (like feathers to the birds), and help in conservation of their body heat. However, in man the heat loss is prevented by the cutaneous sensation of touch. Hairs are distributed all over the body, except for the palms, soles, dorsal surface of distal phalanges, umbilicus, glans penis, inner surface of prepuce, the labia minora, and inner surface of labia majora. The length, thickness and colour of the hairs vary in different part of the body and in different individuals.

Each hair has an implanted part called the *root*, and a projecting part called the *shaft*. The root is surrounded by a *hair follicle* (a sheath of epidermis and dermis), and is expanded at its proximal end to form the *hair bulb*. Each hair bulb is invaginated at its end by the *hair papilla* (vascular connective tissue) which forms the neurovascular hilum of the hair and its sheath. Hair grows at the hair bulb, by proliferation of its cells capping the papilla. The hair follicles, enclosing hair roots, lie obliquely to the surface of the skin, which is responsible for the characteristic hair streams in different parts of the body. The *arrectores pilorum* muscles (smooth muscles supplied by sympathetic nerves) connect the undersurface of the follicles to the superficial part of the dermis. Contraction of these muscles leads to erection of hair, squeezes out the sebum, and produces 'goose skin'. The hair follicle is made up of an outer dermal coat and an inner epidermal coat. The shaft of the hair is made up, from within outwards, of the medulla, cortex (main part) and cuticle.

The foetal skin is covered by fine hairs called *lanugo* (primary hairs). These are mostly shed by birth, and are replaced during infancy by another set of fine hairs called *vellus* (secondary hairs). These are retained in most part of the body, but are replaced by the thick and dark *terminal hair* of the scalp and eyebrows, and other hairy areas of the adult skin. The hairs grow at the rate of about 1.5-2.2 mm per week; their growth is controlled by hormones. The life span of the hair varies from 4 months (eyelashes, axillary hair) to 4 years (scalp hair).

Hairs exhibit alterations in certain diseases. In malnutrition hairs become thin, dry and sparse; in hypothyroidism they become coarse and dry. Excessive growth of hair (*hirsutism*) occurs in adrenogenital syndrome. Loss of hairs is known as *alopecia*.

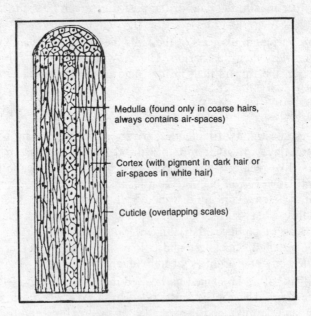

Medulla (found only in coarse hairs, always contains air-spaces)

Cortex (with pigment in dark hair or air-spaces in white hair)

Cuticle (overlapping scales)

Fig. 8.4. Parts of a hair.

3. Sweat Glands (Fig. 8.1B)

Sudoriferous or sweat glands are distributed all over the skin, except for the lips, glans penis, and nail bed. These glands are of two types *eccrine* and *apocrine* (Zelickson, 1971).

The **eccrine glands** are much more abundant and distributed in almost every part of the skin. Each gland is a single tube, the deep part of which is coiled into a ball. The coiled part, called the *body* of the gland, lies in the deeper part of corium or in the subcutaneous tissue. The straight part, called the *duct*, traverses the dermis and epidermis and opens on the surface of the skin. The glands are large in the axilla and groin, most numerous in the palms and soles, and least numerous in the neck and back. The eccrine glands are *merocrine* in nature, i.e., they produce their thin watery secretion without any disintegration of the epithelial cells. They are supplied and controlled by *cholinergic sympathetic nerves*. The glands help in regulation of the body temperature by evaporation of sweat, and also help in excreting the body salts. In dogs, sweat glands are confined to foot pads. Therefore, dogs do not sweat, they pant.

The **apocrine glands** are confined to axilla, eyelids (Moll's glands), nipple and areola of the breast, perianal region, and the external genitalia. They are larger than eccrine glands and produce a thicker secretion having a characteristic odour. They develop in close association with hairs and their ducts typically open into the distal ends of the hair follicles. *Ceruminous glands* of the external auditory meatus are modified apocrine sweat glands. The apocrine glands also are merocrine in nature, but are regulated by a dual autonomic control. Some workers are not inclined to call them as sweat glands at all because they do not respond sufficiently to temperature changes. In animals they produce chemical signals or pheromones, which are important in courtship and social behaviour.

On an average one litre of sweat is secreted per day; another 400 ml of water is lost through the lungs, and 100 ml through the faeces. This makes a total of about 1500 ml, a rough estimate of the invisible loss of water per day. However, in hot climates the secretion of sweat may amount to 3-10 litres per day, with a maximum of 1-2 litres per hour.

So long the sweat glands are intact, the skin can regenerate. If the sweat glands are lost, skin grafting becomes necessary.

Skin is dry in 'Dhatura' poisoning, hear stroke, and diabetic coma; it is unusually moist in hypoglycaemic coma, and peripheral failure.

4. Sebaceous Glands (Fig. 8.1 B)

Sebaceous glands, producing an oily secretion, are widely distributed all over the dermis of the skin, except for the palms and soles. They are especially abundant in the scalp and face, and are also very numerous around the apertures of the ear, nose, mouth, and anus. Sebaceous glands are small and sacculated in appearance, made up of a cluster of about 2-5 piriform alveoli. Their ducts open into the hair follicles, with the exception of lips, glans penis, inner surface of prepuce, labia minora, nipple and areola of the breast, and tarsal glands of the eyelids, where the ducts open on the surface of the skin. Sebaceous glands are *holocrine* in nature, i.e., they produce their secretion by complete fatty degeneration of the central cells of the alveolus, which are then replaced by the proliferating peripheral cells. The secretion is under *hormonal control*, especially the androgens.

The oily secretion of sebaceous glands is called sebum. It lubricates skin and protects it from moisture, desiccation, and the harmful sun rays. Sebum also lubricates hairs and prevents them from becoming brittle. In addition, sebum also has some bactericidal action. Sebum makes the skin water-proof. Water evaporates from the skin, but the fats and oils are absorbed by it.

In *icthyosis* (characterized by abnormally dry skin), the sebaceous glands are few and small, and the secretion of sebum is markedly reduced. Excessive oiliness of skin, due to overactivity of sebaceous glands, is called *seborrhoea*. It may occur from puberty onwards, but diminishes with advancing age. *Acne vulgaris* is a common complication of seborrhoea. Seborrhoeic skin is susceptible to infections (*seborrhoeic dermatitis* or *furunculosis*) and to chemical irritants (chemical folliculitis and dermatitis).

Functions of Skin

1. *Protection.* Skin protects the body from mechanical injuries, bacterial infections, heat and cold, wet and drought, acid and alkali, and the actinic rays of the sun.
2. *Sensory.* Skin is sensory to touch, pain and temperature.
3. *Regulation of body temperature.* Heat is lost through evaporation of sweat; and heat is conserved by the fat and hair.
4. *Absorption.* Oily substances are freely absorbed by the skin.
5. *Secretion.* Skin secretes sweat and sebum.
6. *Excretion.* The excess of water, salts and waste products are excreted through the sweat.
7. *Regulation of pH.* A good amount of acid is excreted through the sweat.
8. *Synthesis.* In the skin, vitamin D is synthesized from ergosterol by the action of ultraviolet rays of the sun.

9. *Storage.* Skin stores chlorides.

10. *Repairative.* The cuts and wounds of the skin are quickly healed.

Applied Anatomy of Skin

1. Skin is pale in *anaemia*, yellow in *jaundice*, and blue in *cyanosis*.

2. *Boil* (furuncle) is an infection and suppuration of the hair follicle and the sebaceous gland.

3. Skin *incisions* should be made parallel to the lines of cleavage. This will result in smallest scars.

4. *Sebaceous cyst* is common in the scalp. It is due to obstruction of the mouth of a sebaceous duct, caused either by trauma or infection.

5. The common *skin diseases* are fungal (like ringworm), allergic (like urticaria, eczema, dermatitis, etc.), and parasitic (like scabies). The usual complaints pertaining to skin are itching, burning, tingling, numbness, etc., and all of them, except for the numbness, indicate varying degrees of irritation of the cutaneous nerves.

6. Loss of touch sensibility is called *anaesthesia*; loss of pain sensibility is called *analgesia*; and loss of temperature sensibility is called *thermanaesthesia*. Exaggerated sensibility is called *hyperaesthesia*, and perverted sensibility, the *paraesthesia*. *Trophic changes* in the skin result from the loss of its sensibility. The skin loses hair, becomes thin and glossy, and may develop ulcers (bedsores), pigmentary changes, and various types of eruptions.

7. Skin grafting is of two types : (a) *Split-thickness skin grafting*, where the greater part of epidermis with the tips of dermal papillae is used; and (b) *full-thickness skin grafting*, where both the epidermis and dermis are used. The donor site in this case is covered with a split-thickness graft. The full-thickness skin graft may be made in the form of a pedicle graft, in which a flap of full-thickness skin is turned and stitched at the recipient site, leaving the base of the flap with its blood supply intact, at the donor site.

Additional points of applied anatomy are discussed under individual heads.

2. SUPERFICIAL FASCIA

Synonyms

1. hypodermis; 2. subcutaneous tissue; 3. tela subcutanea; 4. panniculus adiposus (due to abundance of fat).

Definition

Superficial fascia is a general coating of the body beneath the skin, made up of loose areolar tissue with varying amounts of fat.

Distribution of Fat in this Fascia

1. Fat is *abundant* in the gluteal region (buttocks), lumbar region (flanks), front of the thighs, anterior abdominal wall below the umbilicus, mammary gland (Fig. 8.5), postdeltoid region, and the cervico-thoracic region.
2. In *females*, fat is more abundant and is more evenly distributed than in males.
3. Fat is *absent* from the eyelids, external ear, penis, and scrotum.
4. The subcutaneous layer of fat is called the *panniculus adiposus*.

In females fat is in the superficial fascia of the lower abdomen, upper thigh, whereas in males it is inside the abdominal cavity. In general, in women fat forms a thicker and more even layer than in men. Fat (adipose tissue) fills the hollow spaces like axilla, orbits and ischiorectal fossa. Fat present around the kidneys in abdomen, supports these organs.

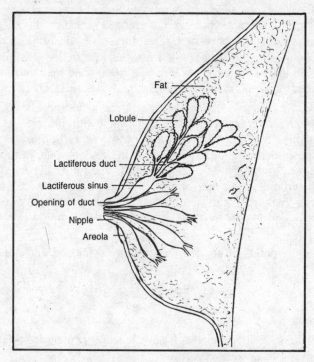

Fig. 8.5. Fat in mammary gland.

Types of Fats

There are two types of fat, i.e., yellow and brown fat. Most of the body fat is yellow, only in hibernating animals it is brown. The cells of brown fat are smaller with several small droplets, and multiple mitochondria. Fat cells are specialised cells, and the size of fat cells increases during accumulation of fat, rather than the number of cells. Any attempt to reduce excessive fat (obesity) must be slow and steady and not drastic, as the latter may cause harm to the body.

Important Features

1. Superficial fascia is *most distinct* in the lower part of the anterior abdominal wall, perineum, and the limbs.
2. It is *very thin* on the dorsal aspect of the hands and feet, sides of the neck, face, and around the anus.
3. It is *very dense* in the scalp, palms, and soles.
4. Superficial fascia shows *stratification* (into two layers) in the lower part of anterior abdominal wall, perineum, and uppermost small part of the thighs.
5. It *contains :* (a) subcutaneous muscles in the face, neck and scrotum; (b) mammary gland; (c) deeply situated sweat glands; (d) localized groups of lymph nodes; and (e) cutaneous nerves and vessels.

Functions

1. Superficial fascia facilitates movements of the skin.
2. It serves as a soft medium for the passage of the vessels and nerves to the skin.
3. It conserves body heat because fat is a bad conductor of heat.

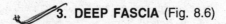

3. DEEP FASCIA (Fig. 8.6)

Definition

Deep fascia is a fibrous sheet which invests the body beneath the superficial fascia. It is devoid of fat, and is usually inelastic and tough.

Distribution

1. Deep fascia is *best defined* in the limbs where it forms tough and tight sleeves, and in the neck where it forms a collar.
2. It is *ill-defined* on the trunk and face.

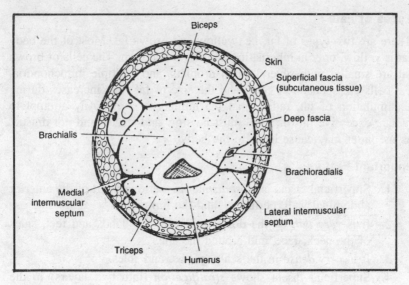

Fig. 8.6. Cross-section of an arm showing the arrangement of superficial and deep fascia.

Important Features

1. *Extensions* (*prolongations*) of the deep fascia form : (a) the intermuscular septa which divide the limbs into compartments; and (b) the fibro-areolar sheaths for the muscles, vessels and nerves.

2. *Thickenings* of the deep fascia form : (a) retinacula (retention bands) around certain joints (wrist and ankle); and (b) the palmar and plantar aponeuroses for protection.

3. *Interruptions* in the deep fascia on the subcutaneous bones. Deep fascia never crosses a subcutaneous bone. Instead it blends with its periosteum and is bound down to the bone.

Modifications of deep fascia are :

Forms the intermuscular septae separating functionally different group of muscles into separate compartments.

Covers each muscle as epimysium which sends in the septae to enclose each muscle fasciculus known as perimysium. From the perimysium septae pass to enclose each muscle fibre. These fine septae are the endomysium. Through all these connective tissue septae, e.g., epimysium, perimysium and endomysium, arterioles, capillaries, venules, lymphatics and nerves traverse to reach each muscle fibre.

Deep fascia covers each nerve as epineurium, each nerve fascicle as perineurium and individual nerve fibre as endoneurium. These connective tissue coverings support the nerve fibres and carry capillaries and lymphatics.

Forms sheaths around large arteries, e.g., carotid sheath, axillary sheath. The deep fascia is dense around the artery and rather loose around the vein to give an allowance for the vein to distend.

Modified to form the capsule, synovial membrane and bursae in relation to the joints.

Forms tendon sheaths/bursae wherever tendons cross over a joint. This mechanism prevents wear and tear of the tendon.

The deep fascia in relation to some joints, e.g., wrist and ankle modified to form thickened bands known as retinacula (Fig. 8.7). These retinacula act as pulleys during the movements of joints.

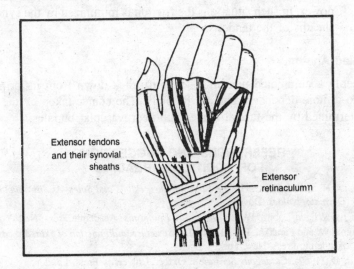

Extensor tendons and their synovial sheaths

Extensor retinaculumn

Fig. 8.7. Extensor retinaculum of wrist.

In the region of palm and sole it is modified to form aponeuroses, e.g., palmar and plantar aponeuroses which afford protection to the underlying structures. It also forms septa between various muscles. These septae are specially well developed in the calf muscles of lower limb. The contraction of calf muscles in the tight sleeve of deep fascia helps in pushing the venous blood and lymph towards the heart. Thus the deep fascia helps in venous and lymphatic return from the lower limb.

In relation to bones, the deep fascia gets continuous with the periosteum of the bare bone. In the forearm and leg, the deep fascia is modified to form the interosseous membrane, which keeps the two bones at optimum distance and increases surface area for attachment of muscles.

Forms investing larger of fascia in relation to neck, giving it proper shape.

Functions

1. Deep fascia keeps the underlying structures in position and preserves the characteristic surface contour of the limbs.
2. It provides extra surface for muscular attachments.
3. It helps in venous and lymphatic return.
4. It assists muscles in their action by the degree of tension and pressure it exerts upon their surfaces.
5. The retinacula act as pulleys and serve to prevent the loss of power. In such situations the friction is minimized by the synovial sheaths of the tendons.

Applied Anatomy

A deeply accumulated pus often tends to track down from its primary site to a more dependent part of the body. The course taken by the pus is determined by the fascial planes and neurovascular bundles.

REFERENCES AND SUGGESTIONS
FOR ADDITIONAL READING

Cummins, H. and Midlo, C. (1961). *Finger Prints, Palms and Soles. An Introduction to Dermatoglyphics*. Dover, New York.

Montagna, W. and Lobitz, W.C. (1964). *The Epidermis*. Academic Press, New York.

Montagna, W. and Parakkal, P.F. (1974). *The Structure and Function of Skin*, 3rd edition. Academic Press, New York.

Sinclair, D. (1967). *Cutaneous Sensation*. Oxford University Press, London.

Zelickson, A.S. (1967). *Ultrastructure of Normal and Abnormal Skin*. Kimpton, London.

Zelickson, A.S. (1971). Ultrastructure of the human epidermis. In : *Modern Trends in Dermatology* (Borrie, P., ed.), Volume 4, Butterworth, London.

9

Connective Tissue, Ligaments and Raphe

1. CONNECTIVE TISSUE

Introduction

Connective tissue is a widely distributed general type of tissue, which supports, binds and protects the special (well differentiated) tissues of the body. It has both the cellular and extracellular components. The cellular component of connective tissue plays the role of active defence, whereas the extracellular component (fibres and ground substance) serves a number of mechanical functions of support and protection against the mechanical stresses and strains. The ordinary type of connective tissue is distributed all over the body, but the special type of connective tissue forms certain well differentiated tissues, like the bone and cartilage. A number of cell types of the connective tissue are also found in the blood and lymph. The greater part of connective tissue develops from embryonic mesoderm. The cells of the connective tissue are widely separated by the abundance of extracellular matrix.

CONSTITUENT ELEMENTS

Connective tissue is made up of cells and extracellular matrix.

A. Cells (Fig. 9.1)

1. **Fibroblasts.** These are most numerous. The cells are flattened and irregular, with branching processes. They *produce collagen fibres*, to which they often adhere, and are particularly active during wound repair. In scurvy, collagen formation is impaired. The old inactive fibroblasts with little cytoplasm are called *fibrocytes.* Reticular cells are similar to fibroblasts, and lay down reticular fibres.

2. **Macrophages (Histiocytes, Clasmatocytes).** These are also quite numerous, and may be 'fixed', or 'motile' (nomadic) in nature, forming a part of mononuclear phagocytic system. The cells are *phagocytic in nature*; when the foreign body is large, they unite together to form multinucleate *giant cells*.

3. **Plasma cells.** These are derived from B-lymphocytes when needed (in pathological states). The cells are oval or rounded, with an eccentric nucleus which has a characteristic 'cartwheel' arrangement of heterochromatin. Plasma cells *produce antibodies*, which may be seen within the cell as *Russel bodies*.

4. **Mast cells (Mastocytes).** These are common in loose connective tissue, serous membranes, and fibrous capsules of certain organs (e.g., liver), and characteristically located around blood vessels. The cells are large and round, with a small nucleus; the cytoplasm is packed with a large number of coarse granules showing metachromasia (resemble basophil leucocytes). Mast cells *produce heparin, histamine* and *serotonin*, and help in the formation of hyaluronic acid of the matrix. These cells are intimately associated with inflammatory, allergic and hypersensitivity reactions.

5. **Fat cells (Lipocytes, Adipocytes).** The cells, filled with a large globule of fat, are signet ring-shaped. They *produce and store fat*.

6. **Pigment cells (Chromatophores)** are the melanocytes which synthesize melanin.

Mesenchyme cells are undifferentiated cells derived from mesoderm. They give rise to practically all varieties of connective tissue cells.

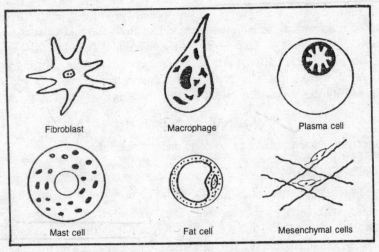

Fig. 9.1. Connective tissue cells.

B. Extracellular Matrix

The matrix has a fibrous and a non-fibrous element. The fibrous element includes three types of fibres, collagen, elastin and reticulin. The non-fibrous element is formed by the ground substance.

1. **Collagen or white fibres.** These are most numerous and widely distributed in various types of ordinary connective tissue, including ligaments, tendons and aponeuroses. These fibres are generally collected in bundles, bound by a mucoprotein. With advancing age the fibres thicken and the mucoprotein diminishes. The soft and flexible collagen fibres are very strong, but are inelastic and inextensible. On boiling collagen fibres swell up and form gelatin (tropocollagen) (Fig. 9.2).

2. **Elastin or yellow fibres.** These fibres are much fewer in number than collagen fibres, and are found in ligamenta flava, elastic arteries, etc. Elastin fibres are formed by fibroblasts, but in the walls of arteries they are formed by the smooth muscle cells. The thin elastin fibres branch and rejoin freely. They are elastic and stretchable, with perfect recoiling. However, elasticity diminishes with age (Fig. 9.2).

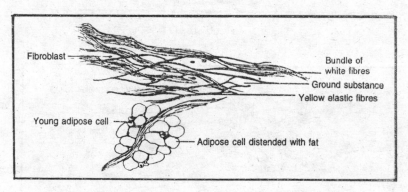

Fig. 9.2. Connective tissue from dermis and subcutaneous layer.

3. **Reticulin fibres.** The fine reticulin fibres branch and anastomose freely to form delicate supporting frameworks of lymphoid organs and many glands. These fibres are laid down by reticular cells which are similar to fibroblasts (Fig. 9.3).

4. **Ground substance.** It is the non-fibrous element of the matrix in which cells and fibres are embedded. In ordinary connective tissue it is a viscous gel containing high proportion of water. Chemically it is made up of mucopolysaccharides, both sulphated and nonsulphated. The sulphated mucopolysaccharides comprise several varieties of chondroitin sulphates and the keratosulphate, whereas the nonsulphated mucopolysaccharide is the hyaluronic acid. The latter is more abundant in loose connective tissue (Fig. 9.4).

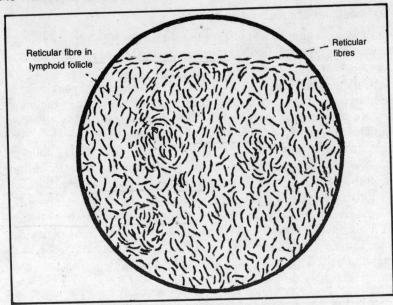

Reticular fibre in lymphoid follicle

Reticular fibres

Fig. 9.3 Reticular tissue-spleen.

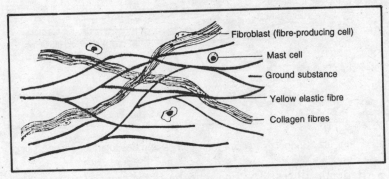

Fibroblast (fibre-producing cell)

Mast cell

Ground substance

Yellow elastic fibre

Collagen fibres

Fig. 9.4. Areolar connective tissue.

TYPES OF CONNECTIVE TISSUE

Different types of connective tissue are found in different parts of the body according to the local functional requirements. These types are based on predominance of the cell type, concentration and arrangement of the fibre type, and character of ground substance. The connective tissues are classified as follows :

I. Ordinary connective tissue

   A. Irregular connective tissue

      1. Loose connective tissue (Fig. 9.4)

      2. Dense irregular connective tissue

      3. Adipose tissue

   B. Regular connective tissue

      Fasciae, ligaments, tendons and aponeuroses (Fig. 9.5-9.7)

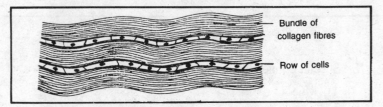

Bundle of collagen fibres

Row of cells

Fig. 9.5. White fibrous connective tissue — L.S. tendon.

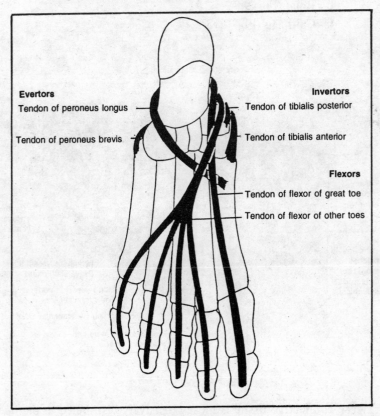

Evertors

Tendon of peroneus longus

Tendon of peroneus brevis

Invertors

Tendon of tibialis posterior

Tendon of tibialis anterior

Flexors

Tendon of flexor of great toe

Tendon of flexor of other toes

Fig. 9.6. Tendons.

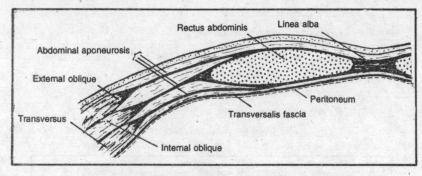

Fig. 9.7. Section of front of abdominal wall above arcuate line.

II. Special connective tissue
   1. Mucoid tissue
   2. Pigmented connective tissue
   3. Bone (Fig. 9.8)
   4. Cartilage (Fig. 2.13-2.17)

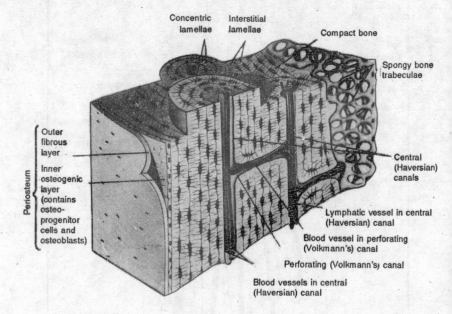

Fig. 9.8. Compact bone.

Loose connective tissue is most extensively distributed in the body. It consists of a network of thin collagen and elastin fibres embedded in a semifluid ground substance along with all varieties of connective tissue cells (except reticular cells). It forms : (a) subcutaneous tissue in the eyelids, penis, scrotum and labia minora; (b) investing sheaths of muscles, vessels and nerves; and (c) internal support of compound glands (binding lobes and lobules), of various coats of hollow viscera, and the fibres of muscles and nerves. Loose connective tissue permits considerable amount of movements between the parts it binds.

Dense irregular connective tissue is found in those parts of the body which are subjected to mechanical stress. The tissue contains a high proportion of collagen fibres with a few fibroblasts. Its blood supply is poor. Dense connective tissue is found in : (a) the reticular layer of dermis; (b) connective tissue sheaths of muscles, vessels and nerves; (c) adventitia of large vessels; (d) capsules of various glands; (e) coverings of various organs such as penis and testis; (b) the sclera of eye; and (g) periostea and perichondria.

Adipose tissue is made up of large groups of fat cells usually arranged in loculi formed by fibrous septa carrying blood vessels. Adipose tissue occurs in abundance in : (a) the superficial fascia of buttocks, loins, nape of neck, breast, lower part of anterior abdominal wall, and front of thighs; (b) fatty capsules of kidney; and (c) mesenteries and omenta. Localized pads of fat occur in the synovial membrane of many joints, and occasional fat cells are widely distributed in the loose connective tissue.

Regular connective tissue is predominantly collagenous, with a few elastic fibres. The regular arrangement of collagen fibres may form sheets (fasciae and aponeuroses) or thicker bundles (tendons and ligaments).

Mucoid tissue is an embryonic type of connective tissue, which forms Wharton's jelly of the umbilical cord, and vitreous body of the eye. The tissue consists of a copious matrix carrying fine meshwork of collagen fibres with fibroblasts.

Pigmented connective tissue occurs in choroid and lamina fusca of the sclera of eye.

FUNCTIONS OF CONNECTIVE TISSUE

1. As a packing material, connective tissue provides a *supporting matrix* for many highly organized structures.
2. It forms *restraining mechanisms* of the body in the form of retinacula, fibrous pulleys, check ligaments, etc.
3. The ensheathing layer of *deep fascia* preserves the characteristic contour of the limbs, and aids circulation in the veins and lymphatics.

4. It provides surface coating of the body in the form of *superficial fascia*, which stores fat and conserves body heat.

5. It provides *additional surface* for the attachment of muscles, in the form of deep fascia, intermuscular septa and interosseous membranes.

6. It forms *fascial planes* which provide convenient pathways for vessels (blood vessels and lymphatics) and nerves.

7. In places where it is loose in texture (loose connective tissue) it *facilitates movements* between the adjacent structures, and by forming bursal sacs it minimizes friction and pressure effects.

8. Connective tissue helps in the *repair of injuries*, whereby the fibroblasts lay down collagen fibres to form the scar tissue.

9. The *macrophages* of connective tissue serve a defensive function against the bacterial invasion by their phagocytic activity. They also act as scavengers in removing the cell debris and foreign material. The *plasma cells* are capable of producing antibodies against specific antigens (foreign proteins), and the *mast cells*, by producing histamine and serotonin, are responsible for the various inflammatory, allergic and hypersensitivity reactions. *Pigment cells* protect the skin against ultraviolet radiation, so that the inflammatory changes typical of sunburn do not occur, and the chromosomal damage in the dividing cells of epidermis are avoided.

10. Connective tissue contains mesenchymal cells of embryonic type. These are capable of transformation into each type of the connective tissue cells with their discrete functions.

2. LIGAMENTS

Definition

Ligaments are fibrous bands which connect the adjacent bones, forming integral parts of the joints. They are tough and unyielding, but at the same time are flexible and pliant, so that the normal movements can occur without any resistance, but the abnormal movements are prevented.

Types of Ligaments

A. According to their composition

1. Most of the ligaments are made up of collagen fibres. These are inelastic and unstretchable.

2. A few ligaments, like the ligamenta flava and ligaments of

auditory ossicles, are made up of elastin fibres (predominantly). These are elastic and stretchable.

B. According to their relation to the joint
1. Intrinsic ligaments surround the joint, and may be extra-capsular or intracapsular.
2. Extrinsic ligaments are independent of the joint, and lie away from it.

Morphology

Ligaments are usually considered as degenerated tendons of the related muscles. Their tendinous nature is evident in some animal ancestors.

Blood and Nerve Supply

The blood vessels and nerves of the joint ramify on its ligaments and supply them.

Most ligaments serve as sense organs because of their rich nerve supply. They act as important reflex mechanisms which are important in monitoring the position and movements of the joint.

Functions

1. Ligaments are important agents in maintaining the stability at the joint.
2. Their sensory function makes them important reflex organs, so that their joint stabilizing role is far more efficient.

Applied Anatomy of Ligaments

1. Undue stretching and tearing of the fibres of a ligament due to an injury is known as 'sprain'. It causes severe pain and effusion into the ligament and joint. The bones are normal as seen in the x-ray film.
2. The joint stability is lost in the neuropathic joints, as occurs in tabes dorsalis, syringomyelia, leprosy, etc.

3. RAPHE

A raphe is a linear fibrous band formed by interdigitation of the tendinous or aponeurotic ends of the muscles. It differs from a ligament in that it is *stretchable*.

Examples : linea alba, pterygomandibular raphe, mylohyoid raphe, pharyngeal raphe, anococcygeal raphe, etc.

APPLIED ANATOMY OF CONNECTIVE TISSUE

1. *Collagen diseases* include rheumatic fever, rheumatoid arthritis, disseminated lupus erythematosus, scleroderma, dermatomyositis, polyarteritis nodosa, and serum sickness. These are the diseases of connective tissue characterized by its fibrinoid necrosis.

2. Inflammations (*fibrositis*) and injuries (*pulls* and *sprains*) of the connective tissue are very painful because of its rich nerve supply or the associated muscle spasm. Relief (healing) of pain in these disorders is markedly delayed due to poor blood supply of the connective tissue.

3. *Marfan's syndrome* is a hereditary disease causing mesodermal and ectodermal dysplasia. It is characterized by excessive height, arachnodactyly, high arched palate, dislocated eye lenses, and congenital heart disease.

REFERENCES AND SUGGESTIONS
FOR ADDITIONAL READING

Garg, K., Bahl, I. and Kaul M., (1991). A Textbook of Histology. CBS Publishers & Distributors

Mitra, N.L. (1979). *A Short Textbook of Histology.* Scientific Book Agency, Calcutta.

Ramachandran, G.N. (1967). *Treatise on Collagen.* Academic Press, New York.

Serafini-Fracassini, A. and Smith, J.W. (1974). *The Structure and Biochemistry of Cartilage.* Churchill-Livingstone, Edinburgh, London.

Wagner, B.M. and Smith, D.E. (1967). *The Connective Tissue* Williams & Wilkins, Baltimore.

10

Principles of Radiography

X-ray are a kind of electromagnetic waves which are used extensively in medicine for both diagnostic and therapeutic purposes. All *electromagnetic waves* (x-rays, ultraviolet rays, infrared rays and radio waves) are produced by acceleration of electrons.

HISTORICAL

X-rays were discovered accidentally on November 8, 1895, by Wilhelm Konrad Roentgen.

Roentgen was a German physicist from the university of Wurzburg. He was engaged in studying the behaviour of an electron beam when passed through a vacuum to strike a tungsten plate. To his surprise he observed that, in addition to electrons, certain unknown rays were also produced, which could pass through the glass envelope of his apparatus and caused a glow on a distant fluorescent screen. He was able to photograph the bones of his hand by placing the hand over a photographic plate and then shining the rays on it. For his unique discovery, Roentgen was awarded the first Nobel Prize in Physics in 1901.

The discovery of x-rays provided a new dimension to the advancement of medical and other sciences. The medical uses of x-rays are both diagnostic and therapeutic. As a diagnostic tool, radiography has proved of great value in detection of the early stages of deep-seated diseases, when the possibility of cure is greatest. Therapeutically, x-rays (radiotherapy) are used in the treatment of cancer (selected cases) because, the rays can destroy cancer cells much more easily than adjacent normal cells.

PROPERTIES OF X-RAYS

The relevant properties of x-rays are as follows.

1. Penetrating Power

X-rays form a part of the spectrum of electromagnetic radiation. They closely resemble the visible light rays in having a similar photographic effect. But they differ from the light rays in being invisible and in having a shorter wave-length. The wave-length of x-rays is 1/10,000 of that of the light rays, i.e., 7.5×10^{-6} - 1.71×10^{-9} cm. It is this property of shorter wave-length which gives them the power of penetration of different materials.

When x-rays pass through the matter, the rays are absorbed to varying extents. The degree of absorption depends on the density (atomic weight) of the matter. Radiography is based on the differential absorption of the x-rays. Dense tissues, like the bone, absorb x-rays far more readily than do the soft tissues of the body. Structures which are easily penetrated by the x-rays are described as *radiolucent*, and the structures which are penetrated with difficulty or are not penetrated at all are described as *radiopaque*. The various structures can be arranged in a scale of increasing radiopacity.

(a) Air, in the respiratory passages, stomach and intestines.

(b) Fat.

(c) Soft tissues, e.g., muscles, vessels, nerves, and viscera.

(d) Bones, due to their calcium content.

(e) Enamel of teeth, and

(f) Dense foreign bodies, e.g., metallic fillings in the teeth, and radiopaque contrast media.

2. Photographic Effect

When x-rays strike a photosensitive film, the film gets photosensitized. When such a film is developed and fixed chemically, a radiography image is obtained.

X-ray film is made up of cellulose acetate, which is coated on its both sides with silver bromide (photosensitive) emulsion 0.001 inch thick. The film is blue tinted and transparent.

An x-ray image (picture) is called skiagram (skia = shadow), radiograph, or roentgenogram. Radiolucent structures produce black shadows, and the radiopaque structures produce white shadows, in the usual negative film. It is useful to remember that gas shadows are black shadows, and bone shadows are the white shadows.

3. Fluorescent Effect

When x-rays strike certain metallic salts (phosphors, like zinc cadmium sulphide), the rays cause them to fluoresce, that is, light rays are produced. This property of x-rays is utilized in fluoroscopy.

4. Biological Effect

X-rays can destroy abnormal cells (e.g., malignant cells) much more easily than the adjacent normal cells. This property of x-rays is utilized in the treatment of various cancers.

However, x-rays are potentially dangerous. On repeated exposures, they can cause burns, tumours, and even mutations. Therefore, adequate protective measures must be taken against repeated exposures to x-rays.

RADIOGRAPHIC VIEWS

Radiographs of a part taken in more than one view give a more complete information about the entire structure by eliminating some particular overlapping shadows in particular views.

The 'view' expresses the direction of flow of the x-rays. In AP (*anteroposterior*) view the rays pass from the anterior to the posterior surface, and the posterior surface faces the x-ray place. In PA (*postero-anterior*) view the x-rays pass from the posterior to the anterior surface, and the anterior surface faces the x-ray plate. The part of the body facing the x-ray plate (i.e., near to x-ray plate) casts a sharper shadow than the part facing the x-ray tube. The chest skiagrams are usually taken in PA view, but for visualizing the thoracic spine, AP view is preferred. The 'view' can also be expressed by mentioning the surface facing the x-ray plate. Thus AP view can also be called as '*posterior*' view, and the PA view as the '*anterior*' view. Similarly, when right surface of the body faces the plate it is called the '*right lateral*' view, and when the left surface of the body faces the plate it is called the '*left lateral*' view. Oblique and other special views are taken to visualize certain special structures.

RADIOGRAPHIC PROCEDURES

1. Fluoroscopy

Fluoroscopy is of special advantage in observing the movements of the organs (lungs, stomach, intestines, etc.), and in changing the position of the subject during the examination. Fluoroscopy is done in a dark room. The fluoroscopic image is visualized directly on the fluorescent screen which is covered with a sheet of lead glass to absorb the x-rays and to protect the fluoroscopist. The sharpness of the fluoroscopic image is inferior to that of a radiograph.

Fluoroscopic image is photographed by a camera in mass miniature radiography (MMR), by which the masses can be surveyed for the detection of diseases such as tuberculosis.

2. Plain Radiography

A natural x-ray image, obtained directly without using any contract medium, is called a plain skiagram, or a plain radiograph. Plain radiography is particularly useful in the study of normal and abnormal bones, lungs, paranasal air sinuses and gaseous shadows in the abdomen (Fig. 10.1).

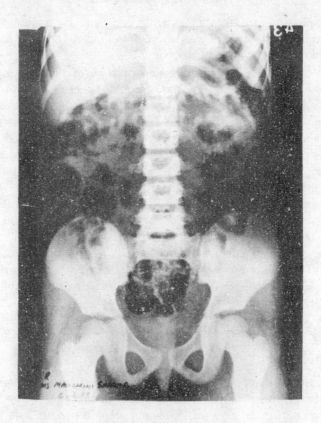

Fig. 10.1. Plain radiography.

Contrast Radiography (Fig. 10.2)

The various hollow viscera and body cavities cannot be visualized in plain radiographs due to their poor differential radiopacity. However, their contrast can be accentuated by filling such organs or cavities with either a radiopaque or a radiolucent substance. Radiography done after artificial accentuation of the contrast is called contrast radiography.

The radiopaque compounds used in contrast radiography are :

1. Barium sulphate suspension (emulsion) in water for gastro-intestinal tract;
2. the aqueous solution of appropriate iodine compounds, for urinary and biliary passages and the vascular system; and
3. the iodized oils (lipiodol and myodil), for bronchial tree, genital passages, subarachnoid space, and ventricles of brain.

The radiolucent contrast media (air, oxygen, nitrogen, carbon dioxide, etc.) are commonly used for visualizing body cavities, like the ventricles of brain and the serous cavities of the body.

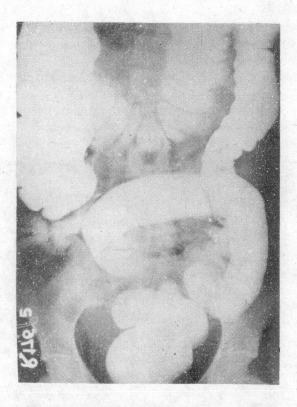

Fig. 10.2. The stomach and small intestine visualised on Barium meal.

Special Procedures (Fig. 10.3)

1. **Computerized tomography (CT scanning).** Computerized tomography is a major technological breakthrough in radiology, especially neuroradiology. It provides images comparable to anatomical slices (3-6 mm thick) of the brain, in which one can distinguish tissues with even slight differences in their radiodensity, viz., CSF, blood, white and grey matter, and the neoplasms. Differentiation between vascular and avascular areas can be enhanced by simultaneous injection of a radiopaque medium in the vessels. Thus CT scanning helps in the diagnosis of the exact location and size of the tumours, haemorrhage, infarction and malformations, including hydrocephalus, cerebral atrophy, etc. This technique is also called as CAT (computerized axial tomography) scanning because it provides images in transverse, or axial, plane.

2. **Xeroradiography.** It provides better images of the soft tissues, like breast (mammographic xeroradiography) and muscles (soft-tissue xeroradiography).

3. **Holography (three dimensional radiography).** It is a type of photography which, with the help of laser beams, provides three dimensional images.

4. **Ultrasonograph.** Ultrasonic diagnostic echography is a safe procedure because instead of x-rays the high frequency sound waves are used. These sound waves are reflected by the acoustic interface (different tissues) back to their source and are recorded in a polarised camera. The

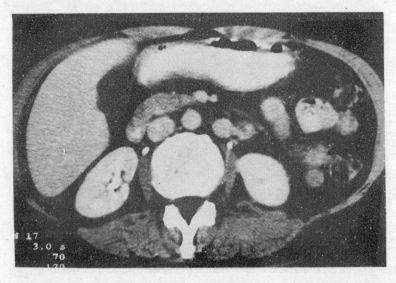

Fig. 10.3. CT scan.

sound waves used are above the range of human hearing, i.e., above 20,000 cycles per second, or 20 kilohertz (hertz = cycles per second). As the technique is quite safe it is especially valuable in obstetric and gynaecological problems (Fig. 10.4 & 10.5).

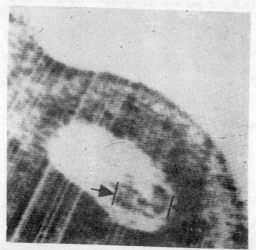

Fig. 10.4. Ultrasonograph. Sagittal scan of the pelvis shows a small fetal pole within a well-formed gestational sac. The arrows indicate the CRL measurement; B indicates the bladder.

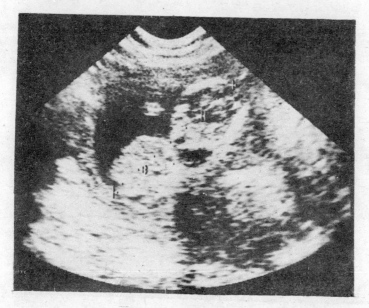

Fig. 10.5. Ultrasonograph.

REFERENCES AND SUGGESTIONS
FOR ADDITIONAL READING

Griffiths, H.J. and Sarno, R.C. (1979). *Contemporary Radiography. An Introduction to Imaging.* Saunders, Philadelphia.

Halim, A. (1993). *Surface and Radiological Anatomy*, 2nd edition. CBS, New Delhi.

11

Anatomical Word Meanings and Historical Names

A	Anglo-Saxon	E	English	It	Italian
Ar	Arabic	F	French	L	Latin
C	Chinese	G	Greek	S	Sanskrit
Du	Dutch	Gr	German		

	Afferent	coming towards
	Anus	ring
(G)	Artery	blood vessel
(L)	Articulation	joint
(G)	Arytenoid	like a pitcher
(G)	Ascitis	bag-like (fluid collection)
	Astrocyte	star-shaped
	Atavism	a remote ancestor (epiphysis)
	Atelectasis	incomplete expansion
	Atheroma	tumour
	Atlas	carry earth on head — 1st cervical vertebra
	Atresia	no hole
(L)	Atrium	central open part
(G)	Atrophy	ill-nourished
(L)	Auditory	related to hearing
	Auerbach (German anatomist)	Auerbach's plexus of autonomic nerves between longitudinal and circular coats of gastro- intestinal tract
(L)	Auricle	diminutive of ear
(L)	Auscultation	to hear with attention
	Autonomic	self-controller

(G)	Autopsy	self-seeing
(L)	Avulsion	to tear away
(L)	Axilla	armpit
(L)	Axis	carry (pillar) — 2nd cervical vertebra
(G)	Azygous	unpaired — A vein in thorax
(F)	Ballotment	tossing
	Basilic	medial vein of arm
	Basophilic	basic stain of nucleus
(L)	Bile	fluid
	Biliverdin	green bile
	Bilirubin	red bile
(G)	Bio	life
	Birth	bearing of offspring
(A)	Bladder	watery swelling
(G)	Blepharitis	eyelid inflammation
(L)	Bolus	mass
(A)	Bone	bar
(F)	Boss	a hump
(G)	Botany	grass
	Bowman (English surgeon)	B. Capsule, B. memb, B. muscle of ciliary body
(L)	Brachium	arm
(G)	Brady	slow
(G)	Brain	upper part of head
(G)	Branchia	gills of fishes — B. arches
(A)	Breast	bursting forth
(A)	Breech	lower part of trunk and thigh
(G)	Bregma	forepart of head
	Brown Sequared (British neurologist)	B.S. syndrome — hemisection of spinal cord
	Broca (French surgeon)	Broca's area — speech centre
(G)	Bronchus	windpipe
(G)	Bronchiole	terminal air tube
(F)	Bruise	to break
	Brunner (Swiss anatomist)	duodenal glands
(L)	Bucia	cheek
(L)	Buccinator	trumpeter
(E)	Buffer	cushion to soften blow
(L)	Bulb	as onion
(L)	Bulbar	medulla oblongata

(L)	Bulbo-cavernosus	
	or	
(L)	Bulbo-spongiosus	accelerator of urine
(L)	Bulla	bubble
(It)	Bunion	swelling
(G)	Burdach (Greek anatomist)	post. column of spinal cord
	Bursa	a purse
(E)	Buttock	end (prominence post. to hip)
(L)	Cadaver	a dead body
(L)	Caecum	blind
	Cesarean section	cutting uterus for taking out a baby (Julius Caesar was born)
(F)	Caisson	box
	Cajal (Spanish histologist)	Cajal stain
(L)	Calamine	red
(L)	Calculus	little stone
(L)	Calvaria	vault of cranium
(L)	Calcaneus	bone of foot
(L)	Calcar	spur (calcarine sulcus)
(L)	Calcar femorale	strong plate of bone in front of lesser trochanter supporting neck of femur (spur-shaped)
(L)	Calcarine fissure	spur-shaped
	Calcination	to make bone
	Calyx	covering of bud/shell
	Calveria	vault
	Camper (Dutch anatomist)	supf. fascia of ant. abd. wall
(L)	Canal	channel or furrow
	Canal of Arnold	for lesser petrosal nerve
	Canal of Schlemm	at cornea-scleral junction
(L)	Cancellous	lattice work
(L)	Cancer	crab-like
(L)	Canine	related to dog (teeth)
	Cannula	hollow, tubular instrument
(L)	Capillary	like hair of head (caput), fine tube
	Capsule	a small box
(L)	Caput	head
	Capitulum	in humerus (lat. part of lower end)
	Caput Medusae	(head of witch) seen because of dilatation of veins at umbilicus due to cirrhosis of liver
(L)	Carbohydrate	made of carbon, hydrogen and water

	Caput succedaneum	swelling produced on presenting part of fetal head during labour
(G)	Cardia	heart
(L)	Caries	decay of bone and teeth
(L)	Carina	structure with a projecting central ridge
(L)	Caro	flesh
(G)	Carotid	to throttle (blood vessel)
	Carotid tubercle	ant. tubercle of 6th cervical vertebra
(L)	Carpus	wrist
(L)	Cartilage	gristle
(L)	Castrate	to cut off
(G)	Catarrh	to flow down
	Catgut	from intestine of sheep
(L)	Cauda	tail
	Caudate	C. nucleus, C. lobe (tail-shaped)
(E)	Caul	cap (fetal membrane with fluid)
(G)	Causalgia	burning pain
(L)	Cavernous	full of compartments
(L)	Cell	small room
	Cement	binding
	Centrifuge	fleeing away from centre
(G)	Centrosome	body centre
(G)	Cephalic	to head (cephalic vein)
(L)	Cera	wax
(L)	Cerebellum	little brain
(L)	Cerebrum	brain
(L)	Cerumen	ear wax
(L)	Cervix	neck, e.g., of uterus, cervical rib
(G)	Chancre	venereal disease
	Chemotaxis	reaction of living cells to chemical agents
	Chest	box
(G)	Chiasma	crossing over
(G)	Chitin	coat
(G)	Chole	bile
(G)	Cholestrin	solid bile
(G)	Chord	a cord of string, e.g., chorda tympani nerve
	Chordata	animals with notochord
(G)	Chorea	dancing (disease of basal gang)
(G)	Chorion	skin
(G)	Chromosome	coloured bodies

(G)	Chyme	juice
	Cilium	eyelid
(L)	Cingulum	girdle
(L)	Circle of Haller	venous circle in areola of female breast
(L)	Circular sinus	sinus around pituitary
	Circle of Willis	arterial circle at base of brain
(L)	Circulation	motion in circle
(L)	Circum	around, e.g., circumflex artery
	Cirrhosis	to turn reddish yellow
	Cisterna	reservoir (at base of brain)
(L)	Claustrum	barrier
	Clavicle	diminutive of key
	Cledio	closes the thorax, clavipect. fascia
(G)	Climacteric	step of a stair (menopause)
	Clinic	at the bed side
	Clinoid	surround pituitary fossa like four posts of bed
(G)	Clitoris	tender (female external genitalia)
(L)	Clivus	slope of a hill — part of cranial fossae
(L)	Cloaca	drain or sewer (dilated part of hindgut)
(G)	Clonus	confused motion
(L)	Coagulation	to curdle
(L)	Coarctation	to press together (C. of aorta)
(G)	Coccyx	cuckoo (coccyx resembles bill of a cuckoo) — lowest part of vertebral column
(L)	Cochlea	snail (internal ear)
(G)	Coelenterate	hollow (internal)
(G)	Coeliac	belly (C. axis artery for stomach)
(G)	Coelome	hollow
	Cohnheim (scientist)	C. areas in skeletal muscle
	Colic	pain in intestine
(G)	Collagen	glue producing substance
	Colloidion	glue-like
	Colon	large intestine
	Colostrum	first milk secreted by breasts
	Colpotomy	cutting through vagina
(L)	Commissure	join together
(L)	Complement	I fill up
(L)	Concha	shell (in lat. wall of nose)
(L)	Concussion	a shaking
(G)	Condyle	knob formed by knuckle of any joint

(L)	Conjugate	yoked together
(L)	Conjunctiva	mucus membrane of eye
(L)	Conus	cone
(G)	Coracoid	a crow-like process of scapula
(L)	Corneum	most superficial layer of epithelium of skin
(G)	Corona	crown, e.g., corona radiata and coronal suture corona glandis (coronary arteries C. sulcus)
(L)	Corpus	body, e.g., C. callosum, C. luteum
(L)	Corpuscle	a little body, pacinian corpuscle, thymic corpuscle
(L)	Corrugator	wrinkler
(L)	Cortex	outer bark (grey matter)
(L)	Cortex	rind (outer layer)
(L)	Costa	rib
(A)	Cough	violent expulsion
	Cowper	C. gland near upper end of male urethra
(S)	Coxa	hip
	Cramp	to contract
(L)	Cranium	skull
(G)	Creatine	(flesh) a non-protein nitrogenous subs. from flesh
(G)	Cremaster	a suspender (of testis)
	Crepitus	a little noise
(L)	Creta	a chalk (CaCO₃)
(F)	Cretin	congenital myxoedema
(L)	Cribriform	sieve-like, e.g., C. fascia of thigh
(G)	Cricoid	ring, e.g., C. cartilage
(L)	Crista	crest
	Crista galli	cock's comb
(L)	Crus	shin bone or leg
(L)	Crural	leg
(L)	Cruciate	cross-like
(L)	Crypt	underground vault (hidden)
(G)	Crystal	clear ice
(L)	Cubitus	elbow
(G)	Cuboid	cube-like
(L)	Culture	growth
(L)	Cuneiform	wedge shape
	Cupola	dome-shaped
(L)	Curriculum	a course of study

(L)	Cusp	point of a spear (cusp of valve)
(L)	Cutis	skin
(F)	Cuvier (anatomist)	ducts of Cuvier
(G)	Cyclops	one-eyed giant
(L)	Cyst	bladder, cystic duct
	Cytoplasm	spread outside the nucleus
(G)	Dacryocyte	tear drop
(G)	Dactylitis	finger inflammation
	Dale (English physician)	histamine discovered by Dale
(E)	Dandruff	skin scabs
(S)	Dartos	leather
	Darwin tubercle	projection in upper part of ear
(L)	Decalcify	process which extracts Ca^{++}
(L)	Deci	one tenth
(L)	Deciduous	falling off
	Decompression	decreased pressure
(L)	Decubitus	lying down
(L)	Decussate	intersection of two lines
(L)	Defecate	to evacuate the bowels
(L)	Degenerate	structural impairment of a tissue
(L)	Deglutition	action of swallowing
	Deiters (German anatomist)	D. cells in internal ear
(G)	Deltoid	triangular in shape, D. muscle, D. lig.
(L)	Dementia	to be mad
(F)	Demilune	half moon, D. of Gianuzzi
(G)	Dendron	tree, dendrites of neuron
	Denonvilliers	fascia between rectum and prostate is D. fascia
(L)	Dens	tooth-like dens of 2nd vet/axis
(L)	Dentate	tooth-like, dentate lig. of piamater, dentate gyrus of brain
(Gr)	Dermis	skin
	Descemets (French surgeon)	D. memb. of cornea
(L)	Desquamate	to scale off
(L)	Detrusor	to thrust away, D. mus of urinary bl.
(L)	Dexter	right
(G)	Diagnosis	thro knowledge
(G)	Dialysis	to loose from one another
(G)	Diapedesis	leading through
(G)	Diaphragm	a partition
(G)	Diaphysis	growing through
(G)	Diarrhoea	flowing through

(G)	Diarthrosis	joint
(G)	Diastole	a pause
(G)	Diathermy	very hot
(G)	Dichotomous	cut in half
(G)	Didelphys	double uterus
(G)	Diencephalon	between brain
(G)	Diet	a way of living
(G)	Digastric	double belly
(L)	Digestion	to dissolve
(L)	Digit	finger
(G)	Diphtheria	leather-like membrane
(G)	Diploe	double layers (D. of some of the skull bones)
(F)	Disease	not well
(L)	Dislocation	pulled out of place
(L)	Dissect	cut apart
(G)	Diuresis	increased urination
(L)	Diverticulum	a small cul-de-sac
(L)	Doctor	a teacher and a healer
(G)	Dolichocephalic	long head
(L)	Dorsum	back
(It)	Douche	to pour
	Douglas (Scottish anatomist)	pouch of Douglas (rectouterine pouch)
(L)	Duct	to conduct
(L)	Duodenum	width of 12 fingers
	Dupuytren (French surgeon)	D. contracture
(L)	Duramater	hard mother
(G)	Dys (prefix)	bad, e.g., dysentery, dyspepsia, dysmenorrhoea
(G)	Ectoderm	outside skin
(G)	Ectopia	displacement (out of place)
(G)	Ectropion	to turn from
(G)	Eczema	anything thrown out by heat
	Edinger (German anatomist)	E. Westphal Nuc. of III N
(L)	Effector	to effect
(L)	Efferent	going away
(L)	Element	a rudiment
(G)	Elephantiasis	elephant-like legs
(G)	Embed	holding in place
(G)	Embolus	a plug
(G)	Embryo	something that grows in another's body
(G)	Emesis	vomiting

(L)	Emissary	escape channels (E. veins connecting intracranial sinuses with extracranial veins)
(L)	Empirical	experienced, not scientific
(L)	Emulsion	milk-like mixture
(F)	Enamel	coating on metal
(F)	Enarthrosis	ball and socket joint
(G)	Encephalon	brain plus head
(G)	Endarteritis	blockage within arteries
(G)	Endemic	native
(G)	Endo (prefix)	within, e.g., endocrine, endolymph, endometrium, endothelium
(G)	Enema	to inject
(L)	Ensiform	sword-like, xiphoid process
(G)	Enteric	gut
(G)	Enuresis	urine passed
(G)	Enzyme	which causes fermentation
(G)	Eosin	pink
(G)	Ependyma	wrap
(G)	Epicondyle	upon a knob
(G)	Epicranius	upon head
(G)	Epicritic	fine touch
(G)	Epidermis	upon dermis
(G)	Epididymis	upon testis
(G)	Epigastrium	upon belly
(G)	Epiglottis	upon tongue
(G)	Epihyal	part of 2nd arch
(G)	Epilepsy	a seizure
(G)	Epinephrine	hormone
(G)	Epiploic	omental
(G)	Episiotomy	cutting the pudendum (perineum)
(G)	Epispadius	upon a tear
(G)	Epistaxis	to trickle
(G)	Epithelium	upon nipple
(G)	Epoophoron	upon egg-bearing
	Erb (German neurologist)	Erb's palsy (C 5, 6)
(L)	Erector	to stand up
(G)	Erotic	love
(L)	Eructation	throwing upwards
(G)	Ethmoid	sieve-like
(G)	Etiology	giving the cause
(G)	Etymology	true analysis of a word

(G)	Euthanasia	painless death
	Eustachius (Italian anatomist)	E. valve
(L)	Evolution	to unroll
(L)	Exacerbation	to irritate
(G)	Exogenous	on the outside
(L)	Experiment	an active test
(L)	Extension	stretch out
(L)	Exteroceptor	outward receptor
(L)	Exude	to sweat out
(L)	Facet	a little face
(L)	Facial	related to face
	Falciform	falx/sickle shaped
	Fallopius (Italian anatomist)	F. tube
(L)	Fascia	a bandage
(L)	Fasciculus	a passage
(L)	Febris	fever
(L)	Femur	thigh
(L)	Fenestra	window
(L)	Ferment	warm
(L)	Fetus	offspring
(L)	Fibula	needle of brooch (bone)
(L)	Filament	small thread
(L)	Filaria	a thread
(L)	Fimbria	a fringe/border
(L)	Fissure	cleft
(L)	Fistula	a pipe
(L)	Flagellum	a whip
(L)	Flatus	to blow
(L)	Flavine	yellow
(L)	Flex	to bend
(L)	Flocculus	a tuft of wool
(L)	Folium	leaf
(L)	Follicle	a bag
	Fontana (Italian anatomist)	spaces of Fontana
(L)	Fontanelle	small fountain
(L)	Foramen	hole
(L)	Forensic	law, courts — F. medicine
(L)	Fornix	an arch
(L)	Fossa	ditch
(L)	Fourchette	little fork
(L)	Fovea	a small pit
(L)	Frenulum	bridle, e.g., F. of tongue, of clitoris, of

		penis
(L)	Frontal	forehead
(L)	Fundus	larger part
(L)	Fundiform	a sling
(L)	Funiculus	cord
(L)	Fusiform	spindle-shaped
(E)	Gag	to suffocate
	Galea	helmet, G. aponeurotica
	Galen (Roman physician)	vein of Galen, (great cb vein)
(A)	Gall	bile
(G)	Gamete	a married person
(G)	Ganglion	a knot
(L)	Gastric	belly
(G)	Gastrocnemius	calf of leg
(G)	Gastrula	belly
(G)	Gene	unit of heredity
	Genetics	study of natural development of race
(L)	Genial	chin
(L)	Genu	bend, knee, (G. of corpus callosum)
(G)	Genus	family
(G)	Geriatrics	old man, G. study and tmt of old persons
(L)	Gestation	carry
(L)	Gingiva	the gums
(L)	Gland	acorn
(G)	Glaucoma	sea green, increased intraocular pressure
(G)	Glenoid	shallow socket
(G)	Glioma	glue
	Glisson (English physician)	G. capsule
(L)	Glomerulus	a ball in kidney
(G)	Glottis	tongue
	Rima	slit
(G)	Gluteal	buttock
(L)	Goitre	the throat
	Golgi (Italian anatomist)	G. stain
	Goll (Swedish anatomist)	Col. of Goll (Fas. gracilis)
	Graaf (Dutch anatomist)	Graafian follicle
(L)	Gracilis	slender
	Graves (Irish physician)	Graves disease
	Gray (English anatomist)	Gray's anatomy
(L)	Gubernaculum	a governor
	Gudden (German neurologist)	G. commissure

(L)	Gustatory	sense of taste
(L)	Gyrus	convolution
(L)	Haeme	blood
	Haematoxylin	stain
(L)	Hallux	big toe
(A)	Hamstring	a little hook
	Hartman (German anatomist)	gall bladder cyst near cystic duct
(L)	Haustrum	bucket-shaped haustration of L. intestine
	Havers (English physician)	Hav. gland — pad of fat in joints
	Heister (German anatomist)	H. valve (in g. bladder)
(G)	Helicotrema	an opening between two scales of cochlea
(G)	Helix	a coil
	Helmholtz (German physician)	H. theory of color vision
	Henle (German anatomist)	H. loop, H. layer in hair follicle
	Hensen (German physician)	H. node
(G)	Hepar	liver
(G)	Hermaphrodite	both sexes
(L)	Hernia	rupture
(G)	Herpes	to spread
(G)	Hetero	different
	Hilton (English surgeon)	H. line
(L)	Hilum	depression
(G)	Hippocampus	sea horse
	Hirschprung (Danish physician)	H. disease (congenital megacolon)
(G)	Histamine	tissue amine
(G)	Histo	anything woven
(G)	Histology	study of woven structures/tissues
(L)	Homo	a man
(G)	Hormone	to set in motion
	Horner (Swiss ophthalmologist)	Horner's syndrome
	Hunter (Scottish surgeon)	H. canal (add. canal)
(G)	Hyaline	glass-like — H. cartilage
(G)	Hybrid	of double origin
(F)	Hydatid	a drop of water
(G)	Hydrocele	water + hernia
(G)	Hygiene	healthy
(G)	Hymen	membrane
(G)	Hyoid	U-shaped

(G)	Hyper	in excess of
	Hypnosis	state of being asleep
(G)	Hypoblast	endoderm
(G)	Hypodermic	under the skin
(G)	Hypothesis	placing under
(G)	Hyster	uterus
(G)	Icterus	a yellow bird (jaundice)
(G)	Idiopathic	unknown
(G)	Idiosyncrasy (allergy)	individual peculiarity
(G)	Ileum	twisted gut
(L)	Ilium	hip bone
(L)	Immunity	exemption or protection
(L)	Incise	to cut into
(L)	Incubation	to sit or brood
(L)	Incus	an anvil (ear ossicle)
(L)	Index	a pointer
(S)	Indigo	blue dye
(L)	Inducium	a tunic
	I. griesum	a grey tunic
(L)	Infant	not speaking
(L)	Infarct	necrotic
(L)	Infection	a bending inward
(L)	Inflame	to set aflame
(L)	Infra	below
(L)	Inguinal	the groin — I. canal
(G)	Inion	below occiput
(L)	Injection	putting in
(L)	Innominate	unnamed
(L)	Inoculate	to ingraft
(L)	Inquest	inquire
(L)	Insanity	unsound mind
(L)	Insemination	seed
(L)	In-situ	manner of lying in local position
(L)	Instrument	to equip
(L)	Insufflation	to blow into
(L)	Insula	island
(L)	Internuncial	inter-messenger
(L)	Intestine	internal
(L)	Intoxication	to smear with poison
(L)	Intra	inside
	Intrinsic	special to the thing itself

(L)	Intussusception	within receive
(L)	Invagination	enclose in a sheath
(L)	Involution	to roll up
(G)	Iodine	violet
(G)	Iris	coloured membrane of eye
(G)	Ischaemia	lack of blood supply
(G)	Ischium	bone (part of hip bone)
(G)	Isotonic	equal tension
(G)	Isotope	equal place
(L)	Isthmus	narrow, I. of fallopian tube
(L)	Iter	a passage (iter cerebri)
(F)	Jaundice	yellowness
(L)	Jejunum	empty or fasting
(L)	Joint	to join
(L)	Jugular	the throat
	Jugam	yoke
(G)	Karyo	a nut (nucleus)
	Keith (English anatomist)	SA node
(G)	Keratin	horn-in hairy layer of skin
(G)	Kilo	one thousand
	Klumpke (French neurologist)	K. paralysis
	Kupffer (Greek anatomist)	K. cell (sinusoids of liver)
	Kymograph	a wave writer
(G)	Kyphosis	hump on back
(L)	Labrum	lip
	Labial	pertaining to lips
(L)	Labour	work
(L)	Lac	milk
(G)	Labyrinth	maze
(L)	Lacrimal	tear
(L)	Lacunae	hollow
(G)	Lambda	inverted Y-shaped L. suture
(L)	Lamina	a thin plate
(L)	Lancet	a slender spear
	Langerhans (German anatomist)	islet of Langerhans (pancreas)
(L)	Lanugo	first soft hair of beard
(L)	Larva	ghost
(G)	Larynx	upper parts of wind pipe

(L)	Latent	to lie hidden
(L)	Laxative	loosening
(Gr)	Lemniscus	bandage
(Gr)	Leprosy	scaly disease
(Gr)	Leptomeninx	tender membrane (pia and arachnoid)
(L)	Lethal	death
(Gr)	Lethargy	forgetful
(Gr)	Leuc	white, leucocyte, leucoplakia, leucorrhoea
(L)	Levator	one who lifts
(L)	Libido	desire, lustre
(G)	Lieberkuhn (German scientist)	crypts of Lieberkuhn (intestine)
(L)	Lienal	spleen
(L)	Ligament	to bind, e.g., deltoid lig, falciform lig, etc.
(L)	Limbus	a border
(L)	Limen	edge or threshold — L. insulae
(L)	Linea	a line
(L)	Lingual	the tongue
(S)	Lipoma	fat
(Gr)	Lithos	a stone
(L)	Locus	a place
(G)	Lordosis	increased anterior curvature of lumbar spine
	Louis (French physician)	angle of sternum (sternal angle)
	Lower (English physician)	projection in the right atrial wall between the two caval openings
	Ludwig (German surgeon)	L. angina
(L)	Lumbar	loin
	Lumbrical	a worm (a muscle)
(L)	Lumen	light passage
(L)	Lunar	the moon
	Lutein (German anatomist)	yellow pigment of corpora lutea
(L)	Lymph	clear water
(Gr)	Macro	big
	Macroscopic	big to see
(L)	Macula	a small patch (macula lutea, macula densa)
	Magendie (French doctor)	F. of Magendie
(G)	Malacia	softness
(F)	Malady	illness

(L)	Malar	cheek bone
	Malaria	bad air
(L)	Malignant	ill-disposed
(L)	Malleus	hammer — ear ossicle
(L)	Mallelous	a little hammer
	Mallory (Irish anatomist)	M. stain
	Malphigian (Italian anatomist) — Founder of Histology	M. corpuscle, M. layer in skin
(L)	Mamma	the breast
(L)	Mandible	lower jaw
(Gr)	Mania	madness
(L)	Manubrium	a handle (M. sterni)
(Gr)	Marasmus	waste away
	Marchi (Irish anatomist)	M. staining for nerve fibres
	Marginal	artery border, along large intestine
(L)	Marrow	medulla
	Marshall (English surgeon)	M. vein — oblique vein of left atrium
(Gr)	Masseter	the chewer
(Gr)	Mast	to feed
(Gr)	Mastos	breast
(L)	Mastication	to chew
(L)	Matrix	mould
(L)	Mature	to ripe — maturation
	Maxilla	cheek
	McBurney (American surgeon)	M. point for appendicectomy
(L)	Meatus	canal
	Meckel (German anatomist)	M. cave for 5th N. ganglion, M. cartilage
	Meatus	canal
(L)	Median	central
(L)	Mediastinum	middle space
(L)	Medicine	the art of healing
(L)	Medulla	marrow
	Medusa (Greek goddess)	caput Medusa
(G)	Mega	big
	Meibom (German anatomist)	Meibomian glands
(G)	Meiosis	lessening
	Meissner	M. plexus in submucous coat of GIT
(G)	Melan	black
	Melanin	black pigment

(G)	Meninges	a membrane
	Meningocoele	memb. + hernia
(G)	Meniscus	crescent (med. cat. menisci in knee joint)
(G)	Men (prefix)	month, e.g., menopause, menorrhagia, menstruation menarche
(Gr)	Merkel	corpuscle sensory nerve ending
(Gr)	Mesencephalon	mid-brain
(Gr)	Mesenchyme	middle infusion or juice
(Gr)	Mesentery	middle intestine
	Mesoderm	middle skin
(G)	Mesonephros	middle kidney
(G)	Mesothelium	middle nipple
(G)	Metacarpus	from wrist
(G)	Metamorphosis	changed form
(G)	Metanephros	after kidney
(G)	Metastasis	removal from one place
(G)	Metencephalon	after brain
(G)	Metopic	space between eyes — M. suture
(G)	Metre	unit of length
	Meynert (Austrian physician)	Dorsal teg. decusation
(G)	Microbe	small life
(G)	Microcyte	small cell
(G)	Microglia	small glue (cells)
(G)	Micrometer	small measure
(G)	Microscope	small eye-view
(G)	Microtome	small cutting
(G)	Mitochondria	the thread grain
(G)	Mitosis	thread
(L)	Mitral	kind of cap
(G)	Mneomonic	relating to memory
(L)	Molar	milestone — a tooth
(E)	Mole	spot
	Monro (English scientist)	foramen of Monro — interventricular foramen of brain
	Montgomery (Irish obstetrician)	M. tubercles in the nipple
(L)	Morbid	ill
	Morgagni (Italian anatomist)	appendix of testis
(F)	Morgue	mortuary
	Morison (English surgeon)	Morison's pouch (hepatorenal pouch)
(G)	Moron	dull

(G)	Morphology	shape/discourse
(L)	Morula	mulberry
(L)	Mucus	thin watery fluid, mucosa
	Muller (German anatomist)	M. muscle in eye (circular) Mullerian duct
(L)	Multiparous	more than once pregnant
(L)	Murmur	a humming sound
(L)	Muscle	a little mouse; myology
(G)	Museum	temple of muses
(L)	Mutation	to change
(L)	Mydriatic	unnatural dilatation of pupil
(G)	Myopia	close to eyes
(G)	Myxoma	mucus + tumor
	Naboth (German anatomist)	Nabothian glands
(L)	Naevus	birth mark
	Nagek (German obstetrician)	Nagek pelvis (obliquely contracted pelvis)
(E)	Nape	ext. depression, knob
	Narcolepsy	numbness
(L)	Nares	nostril, nasal
(G)	Nausea	sickness
(A)	Navel	umbilicus
(L)	Navicular	boat-shaped
(G)	Necrosis	a dead body
(G)	Neo	new
	Neolithic	new stone
	Neoplasm	new form
(G)	Nephr	kidney
	Nephropexy	kid + fastening
(L)	Nerve	string, N. root
(G)	Neuralgia	pain in nerves
(G)	N. crest	on either side of neural tube
(G)	Neurasthenia	nerve weakness
(G)	Neurilemma	nerve covering
(G)	Neurobiotaxis	nerve + life + arrangement of nerves in living
(L)	Neutrophil	neuter (not fond of any color)
	Nipple	beak
	Nissls (German neurologist)	N. granules in neurons
(L)	Nodus	knot
(L)	Nomenclature	a list of names
(G)	Nostalgia	home coming + pain

(G)	Notochord	back + a string
(Ar)	Nucha	spinal cord
(Du)	Nuck	canal of Nuck
(L)	Nucleus	nut
(L)	Nullipara	none + bring forth, not yet pregnant
(L)	Nurse	to nourish
(G)	Nyctalopia	night blindness
(G)	Nystagmus	nodding
(Gr)	Obelian	a pointed pillar portion of sagittal suture between 2 parietal bones
(L)	Obstetrics	midwife
(L)	Obturator	a stopper of
(L)	Occiput	back of head
(L)	Occult	hidden
(L)	Oculus	eye
	Oddi (Irish physician)	sph. of Oddi
(G)	Odontoid	tooth-like
(G)	Oesophagus	gullet
(L)	Oestrus	madness or frenzy
(G)	Olecranon	point of elbow
(L)	Olfaction	to smell
(G)	Oligo	few
(G)	Omohyoid	shoulder + hyoid bone
(G)	Omphalos	omphalocoele (umb.)
(G)	Oopheron	ovary
(L)	Operation	to work
(L)	Operculum	lip
(Gr)	Ophth	eye
(Gr)	Optics	belonging to sight, O. chiasma; O. disc
(L)	Oral	of mouth
(L)	Orbicularis	circular
(G)	Orchitis	testicle inflammations
(L)	Organ	any part of the body with a special function
(Gr)	Osmosis	push
(L)	Ossicle	small bone
(Gr)	Otic	ear, O. ganglion
(L)	Ovary	egg receptacle
(G)	Oxyntic	to make sour
	Pacchioni (Italian anatomist)	arachnoid granulations

(Gr)	Pachymeninx	thick membrane
	Pacini (Italian anatomist)	P. bodies
(G)	Paediatrics	child + healing
	Paget (English surgeon)	P. disease
(G)	Palaco	old
(L)	Pallid	pale
(L)	Pallium	clock or mantle
(L)	Palpate	to touch
(L)	Palpebra	eyelid
	Palsy	paralysis
(L)	Pampiniform	tendril
(G)	Penacea	all healing
(G)	Pan	sweet bread
(G)	Pandemic	all people
(L)	Panniculus	a piece of cloth, P. carnosus
(L)	Paraffin	little affinity
	Paradidymus	beside + twin-like
(Gr)	Paralysis	weakening
	Parametrium	beside the uterus
	Paraphimosis	constriction of the prepuce behind the glans penis
	Paraplegia	paralysis of lower limbs
	Parenchyma	functional
	Parietal	a wall
	Paronychia	beside nail
	Para	beside
	Passavant (German surgeon)	P. ridge
(L)	Patella	a small dish (sesamoid bone)
(L)	Pecten	a comb
(L)	Pectoral	belonging to breast
(L)	Pedicle	a little foot
	Peduncle	a foot
	Pellagra	skin attack
(L)	Pelvis	a basin
(L)	Penis	tail
(L)	Percussion	beating
(L)	Perforator	to bore through
(G)	Peri	around
(G)	Perilymph	clear watery fluid all around
(G)	Perineum	swim around penis
(G)	Periosteum	around bone

(G)	Periphery	circumference
	Peristalsis	contracting around
	Peritoneum	serous membrane lining abdomen
(G)	Peroneus	anything pointed for piercing
(L)	Pes-a foot	hippocampus (foot-like)
(L)	Pessary	an oval body (plug)
	Petit (German surgeon)	P. triangle
(L)	Petrous	stony, rock, P. temporal bone
	Peyer (German physician)	P. patch (ileum)
(G)	Phagocytosis	eat + cell + osis (fullness), i.e., eating cells
(G)	Phalanx	closely knit row
(G)	Pharynx	musculo memb. sac behind the mouth
(L)	Philtrum	a love charm
(Gr)	Phimosis	stopping up (in relation to prepuce of penis)
(Gr)	Phonation	sound or voice
(Gr)	Physiotherapy	nature + treatment
(L)	Pia mater	soft mother
(L)	Pineal	pine cone
(L)	Pinna	ear
(L)	Piriform	pear-shaped
(L)	Pisiform	pea-shaped
(L)	Pituitary	mucus secretion
(L)	Placenta	flat cake
	Planes	flat
	Plantar	sole of foot
(Gr)	Platysma	flat
(Gr)	Pleo	more
(Gr)	Plithora	fullness
(Gr)	Pleura	serous memb. enfolding lung
(L)	Plexus	woven
(L)	Plica	to fold
(L)	Plumbus	lead
(Gr)	Pneumo	gas
(Gr)	Podagra	foot
(Gr)	Podalic	foot
(L)	Polarity	relating to pole
(Gr)	Polio	grey matter + inflammation
(L)	Pollex	thumb (strong)
(Gr)	Poly	many
(L)	Pons	bridge

(L)	Popliteus	ham
(L)	Porta	gate
(L)	Post	behind
	Poupart (French surgeon)	P. ligament (inguinal ligament)
(L)	Pregnant	with child
(L)	Prepuce	foreskin
(Gr)	Presbyobia	old age hypermetropia
(Gr)	Proposis	elephant's trunk
(L)	Process	advance
(L)	Procidentia	parts that fall out of place
(Gr)	Prodo	anus
(Gr)	Prodromal	in advance
(L)	Progesterone	before to bear
(Gr)	Prognosis	to know beforehand
	Prolapse	falling
(L)	Proliferato	I bear
(L)	Promontory	prominence
(L)	Pronator	to bend forward
(Gr)	Pronephros	before kidney
(Gr)	Prophylaxis	to keep guard (the prevention of a disease)
(L)	Proprioceptive	one's own, to take
(Gr)	Prosencephalon	forward + brain
(Gr)	Prostate	before + stand
(Gr)	Prosthetic	in addition
(Gr)	Protamine	first + amine
(Gr)	Protein	comprised of amino acid
(Gr)	Protocol	first glue
(Gr)	Protopathic	first + suffering
(L)	Pruritis	itching
(Gr)	Psoas	loin
	Psyche	breath
(Gr)	Pterion	wing
(Gr)	Pterygoid	wing-like
(Gr)	Ptoma	a corpse
(Gr)	Ptosis	falling
(Gr)	Ptyalin	saliva
(L)	Pubis	puberty
(L)	Pud	to be ashamed (pudeudal)
(L)	Puerperal	after delivery
(E)	Puke	to vomit
(L)	Pul (prefix)	lung
(L)	Puke	beating

(L)	Pulvinar	cushion, pillow
(L)	Punctum	point
(L)	Putamen	cutting
(Gr)	Pyelo	basin
(Gr)	Pylorus	gatekeeper
(Gr)	Pyramid	swelling
(Gr)	Pyrexia	fever
(L)	Quadri	four
	Quadratus	square
	Quadriceps/Quadri	geminus four heads/two twins
(G)	Quartz	rock crystal
(L)	Rabies	rage/madness
(L)	Racemose	cluster of grapes (glands)
(Gr)	Rachitis	spine
(L)	Radical	roots
(L)	Radium	radioactive element
(L)	Radius	small bone of forearm
(L)	Ramus	branch
	Ranvier (French histologist)	node of Ranvier
(Gr)	Raphe	suture
(L)	Rash	eruption of skin
	Rathke (German anatomist)	R. pouch
(L)	Receptor	to receive
(L)	Rectum	upright (misnomer)
(L)	Recurrent	running back
(L)	Refraction	broken (bend)
	Reid (Scottish anatomist)	R. base (from lower margin of orbit through centre of ext. aud. meatus)
	Reil (Greek physiologist)	island of Reil-Insula
	Reissner (Greek anatomist)	R. fibres running through the length of brainstem and spinal cord
	Remarc (German neurologist)	R. fibre/non-medullated nerve fibre
(L)	Resection	cut off
(L)	Resin	to flow
(L)	Restiform body	rope-shape (inferior cerebellar peduncle)
(L)	Rete	a net, R. mirabile — a wonderful network, R. testis — tubular network
(L)	Reticulum	a little net
(L)	Retinaculum	to hold back
(L)	Retort	twisted back

(L)	Retro (prefix)	behind, R. verted, retroflexed uterus, retroph. space
	Retzius (Swedish scientist)	space of Retzius
(Gr)	Rheumatism	a liability
(Gr)	Rhinencephalon	nose + brain
(Gr)	Rhinoplasty	nose moulding
(Gr)	Rhomboid	rhombus-like
(Gr)	Rhonchus	snoring
(L)	Rigor	rigidity
(L)	Rima	slit, R. glotlidis
(L)	Risus	to laugh, risus sardonicus
	Robertson (Scottish ophthalmologist)	R. pupil
	Robin (German histologist)	perivas/space in brain
	Rolando (Italian anatomist)	fissure of Rolando
	Rosenmuller (German anatomist)	fossa of Rosenmuller (Lat. pharyngeal recess)
(L)	Rostrum	beak of a bird
(L)	Rubella	red
	Ruffini (Italian anatomist)	nerve endings of skin
(L)	Rugat	wrinkled
(L)	Saccharin	sugar
(L)	Sacrum	holy
(L)	Sagittal	arrow
(Gr)	Salpina	trumpet
	Santorini (Italian anatomist)	S. cartilage, santorini duct acc. duct of pan.
(Gr)	Saphenous	clear, easily seen, S. vein
(Gr)	Sarco	flesh, sarcolemma
(L)	Sartorius	tailor
(L)	Scala	stairway (scala tympani, scala vestibule)
(Gr)	Scalenus	irregular
(L)	Scalpel	knife
(Gr)	Scaphoid	boat-shaped
(L)	Scapula	shoulder blades
	Scarpa (Italian anatomist)	S. fascia, (deeper membranous layer of sup. fascia) Sc. ganglia 8th N. ganglia
(Gr)	Schizophrenia	split mind
	Schlemm (German anatomist)	canal at corneo-scleral junction
	Schwann (German anatomist)	sheath of Schwann
(L)	Sciatica	pain in loins
(L)	Scirrhus	hard

(L)	Stricture	contraction
(L)	Strider	harsh
(Gr)	Stroma	bed
(Gr)	Styloid	pointed
(L)	Sub	under
(L)	Subclavian	under clavicle
(L)	Substantia	essence
(L)	Sudor	sweat
(L)	Sulcus	furrow
(L)	Super	over, above
(L)	Supination	bent backwards
(L)	Sural	calf of leg
(Gr)	Surgeon	hand + work (operator)
(L)	Sustentaculum	support (sus. lig)
(L)	Stitch	sewing together
	Sylvius (German anatomist)	Lat. fissure of the brain
(Gr)	Symbiosis	living with
(Gr)	Symphysis	natural union
(Gr)	Syndrome	running together
(G)	Synovia	along with + egg
(L)	Syringe	like a pipe (tube)
(Gr)	Syringomyelia	pipe + marrow
(Gr)	Systole	contraction
(L)	Tabes	wasting away
(Gr)	Taenia	rope-like structure, T. thalami, T. coli, hookworms
(L)	Talipes	weak on feet
(L)	Talus	ankle bone
(L)	Tapetum	carpet
(Gr)	Tarsus	crate — bones of post. part of foot
(L)	Tectum	to cover
(Gr)	Telangiectesis	end vessel dilatation
(L)	Tellurium	earth
(L)	Temple (temporal)	temple region
(L)	Tendon	to stretch out
	Tenon (German surgeon)	T. capsule (back of eyeball)
(L)	Tensor	stretch out
(L)	Tentorium	tent
(L)	Teres	round
(L)	Testicle	testis (singular)
(Gr)	Tetanus	stretch, tetany

(Gr)	Sclera	hard
(Gr)	Scoliosis	curvature (lateral)
(L)	Scrotum	skin or hide
(L)	Sebum	grease
(L)	Segmentation	to cut
(L)	Sella turcica	Turkish saddle
(L)	Semen	that which is sown
(L)	Semi	half
(L)	Septum	a dividing wall
(L)	Serratus	like saw
(Gr)	Sesamoid	seed-like (patella)
	Sharpey (English anatomist)	S. fibres in compact bone
	Sibson	S. fascia
(Gr)	Sigmoid	sigma-like
	Sims position	lithotomy position
(L)	Sinus	anything hollowed out
(Gr)	Skeleton	dried up
(L)	Soleus	sole
(Gr)	Soma	body
(L)	Soporific	deep sleep
(L)	Spatula	flat wooden instrument
(Gr)	Sperm	seed
	Sphenoid	wedge-shaped
(Gr)	Sphincter	bind/tight
(L)	Spine	thorn
(Gr)	Splanchnic	relating to bowels
(Gr)	Splenius	bandage
(Gr)	Spondylitis	vertebra inflammation
(Gr)	Spondylolisthesis	vet + sliding
(L)	Squama	scale of fish
(L)	Stapes	stirrup (ear ossicle)
(Gr)	Stasis	standing
(Gr)	Stenosis	narrowing
	Stenson (Danish anatomist)	parotid gland duct
(Gr)	Stethoscope	instrument of listening the ausculatory sounds
(L)	Stimulus	to prick
(Gr)	Stoma	mouth
(Gr)	Stomach	mouth bed
(Gr)	Strabismus	squinting
(L)	Stratum	covering
(L)	Stria	furrow

(Gr)	Thalamus	inner chamber
(Gr)	Thallium	young
	Thebesius (German physician)	valve of coronary sinus
(Gr)	Thenar	the part of the hand with which one strikes
(Gr)	Theory	speculation
(Gr)	Therapy	care
(Gr)	Thrombus	rump
(L)	Thymus	leaf used for worship
(Gr)	Thyroid	shield (oblong)
(L)	Tibia	shin bone (flute)
(Gr)	Tissue	woven
(Gr)	Tone	which can be stretched
(A)	Tooth	an organ of mastication
(Gr)	Topography	a place + description
(L)	Torticollis	twisted
(L)	Torus	bulging place
(Gr)	Tourniquet	instrument for turning
(Gr)	Toxin	poison
(L)	Trabeculae	a little beam
(Gr)	Trachea	wind pipe
(L)	Tract	pathway
(Gr)	Tragus	ear
(L)	Transfusion	pouring out
	Trapezium	table
(Gr)	Trauma	wound
	Treitz (Austrian physician)	lig of Treitz at Duo-jej. flexure
(Gr)	Trema	hole
(L)	Tremor	shaking
	Trendelenburg (German surgeon)	T. position, T. sign and T. test
	Trephine	a saw for cutting out circular piece of bone esp. skull
	Treves (English surgeon)	bloodless fold of Treves
(L)	Triceps	having three heads
(Gr)	Trichiasis	hair (trichionis)
(L)	Tricuspid	three cusps
(L)	Trigeminal	three + twin-like (3 divisions)
(Gr)	Trigone	triangle
(L)	Triquetral	having 3 corners
(Gr)	Trocar	3 quarters

(Gr)	Trochanter	bony process
(L)	Trochlea	pulley
(Gr)	Trophic	nourishment (trophoblast)
(Gr)	Tropism	burning
(L)	Tube	a trumpet
(L)	Tumour	swelling
(L)	Turbinate	spinning top
(L)	Tympanum	kettle drum
	Typhoid	fever typhus like
	Tyson (English anatomist)	seb. glands on inner side of prepuce
(L)	Ulcer	sore
(L)	Ulna	elbow
(L)	Umbilicus	naval
	Umbo	tymp. membrane
(L)	Unciform	hook-shaped
(L)	Undulant	fever, wave
(Gr)	Urachus	urinary canal of foetus
(Gr)	Uranium	heaven
(Gr)	Ureter	urinary duct
(Gr)	Urethra	to make water
(Gr)	Urobilin	urine + bile
(L)	Urticaria	to burn
(L)	Uterus	womb
	Utricle	a little uterus
(L)	Uvea	grape
(L)	Uvula	a little grape
(L)	Vaccine	lymph from cow-pox vesicle
(L)	Vagina	sheath
(L)	Vagus	vagabond (wanderer)
(L)	Valency	capacity
	Valentine (German physician)	discovered nucleolus and sex cords of ovary
	Valentine (German anatomist)	V. bodies in N. tissue
(L)	Valgus	bow legged
	Valsalva (Italian anatomist)	V. sinuses aortic sinuses
(L)	Valve	leaf of folding door
(L)	Varix (varicose)	dilated veins
	Varolius (Italian anatomist)	pons varolii
(L)	Varus	grown inwards knock knee — genu Varus

(L)	Vas	vessel
(L)	Vastus	large
	Vater (German anatomist)	amp. of Vater
(L)	Vector	one that bears
(L)	Velum	curtain
(L)	Venereal	belonging to Venus (goddess of love)
(L)	Venter	belly, ventricle
(L)	Vermis	worm
(L)	Vertebra	turning place or joint
(L)	Vertigo	to turn around
	Vesalius (Belgian anatomist)	Father of Anatomy
(L)	Vesica	bladder
(L)	Vestibule	enclosed space
(L)	Vestigeal	remnant of something formerly present
(L)	Veterinary	cattle doctor
	Vidius (Italian physician)	N. of pterygoid canal
(L)	Villus	tuft of hair
	Virchow (German pathologist)	V. robin space
(L)	Virus	poison
(L)	Viscus/viscera	vital organ/plural
(L)	Vision	act of seeing
(L)	Vital	to life
(L)	Vitamin	life + amine
(L)	Vitelline	yolk of egg
(L)	Vocal cords	uttering of voice
(L)	Volar	palm of hand
	Volkmann (German physician)	V. canal
(L)	Voluntary	willing
(L)	Volvulus	to roll
(L)	Vomer	thin plate of bone between nostrils
(L)	Vulva	to roll, to turn around
	Waldeyer (German anatomist)	W. ring at oropharyngeal isthmus
	Waller (English physician)	Wallerian nerve degeneration
	Westphal (German neurologist)	W. nucleus (part of oculomotor complex)
	Wharton (English anatomist)	W. duct (submand. duct), Wharton's jelly
	Whisky	water of life
	Whitlow	painful swelling in finger

(E)	Whooping cough	to call/shout
	Widal (French physician)	W. reaction
	Willis (English anatomist)	circle of Willis
	Winslow (Danish anatomist)	foramen of Winslow
	Wirsung (German anatomist)	pancreatic duct
	Wistar (American anatomist)	pyramids (in kidneys)
	Wolff (German anatomist)	Wolfian or mesonephric
	Wright	W. stain
	(American pathologist)	
(Gr)	Xanthine	yellow
	Xeroderma	dry or parched
(Gr)	Xiphoid	sword-like
	Xylol	wood + oil
	Yellow fever	an infectious viral fever
	Young (English physician)	Young's rule
	Zenker (German pathologist)	Z. solution
	Zinn (German anatomist)	annulus of Zinn (origin of rectus)
(L)	Zona	zone
(Gr)	Zoology	animal + treatise
	Zuckerkandl	Z. gyrus — subcallosal gyrus
	(Austrian anatomist)	
	Zygoma	like a yoke
	Zymogen	ferment producer, Z. granules in serous acini

Index